U316 Book 2

The Open University

BIODIVERSITY AND ECOSYSTEMS

edited by
Jonathan Silvertown

THE ENVIRONMENTAL WEB  U316

Cover images courtesy of Mike Dodd. From left to right: New Zealand rain forest; mushroom (*Mycena galericulata*); Siberian tiger (*Panthera tigris altaica*); banded demoiselle (*Calopteryx splendens*).

This publication forms part of an Open University course U316 *The Environmental Web*. The complete list of texts which make up this course can be found on the back cover. Details of this and other Open University courses can be obtained from the Course Information and Advice Centre, PO Box 724, The Open University, Milton Keynes MK7 6ZS, United Kingdom: tel. +44 (0)1908 653231, e-mail general enquiries@open.ac.uk

Alternatively, you may visit the Open University website at http://www.open.ac.uk where you can learn more about the wide range of courses and packs offered at all levels by The Open University.

To purchase a selection of Open University course materials visit the webshop at www.ouw.co.uk, or, contact Open University Worldwide, Michael Young Building, Walton Hall, Milton Keynes MK7 6AA, United Kingdom for a brochure: tel. +44 (0)1908 858785; fax +44 (0)1908 858787; e-mail ouwenq@open.ac.uk; website http://www.ouw.co.uk

The Open University
Walton Hall, Milton Keynes
MK7 6AA

First published 2003

Edited, designed and typeset by The Open University.

Printed and bound in the United Kingdom by The Bath Press, Glasgow.

ISBN 0 7492 56796

1.1

u316 book 2i1.1

1399042X

U316 *The Environmental Web* Course Team

Course Team Chair

Jonathan Silvertown, Department of Biological Sciences, Faculty of Science

Course Managers

Tracy Finnegan, Department of Biological Sciences, Faculty of Science
Marion Hall, Department of Biological Sciences, Faculty of Science

Course Team Assistant

Catherine Eden, Department of Biological Sciences, Faculty of Science

Open University Authors

Mark Brandon, Department of Earth Sciences, Faculty of Science
(Chair and author Block 1)
Nigel Clark, Department of Geography, Faculty of Social Science (Block 1)
Mike Dodd, Department of Biological Sciences, Faculty of Science (Block 2)
Marion Hall, Department of Biological Sciences, Faculty of Science (Block 1)
Stephen Peake, Department of Design and Innovation, Faculty of Technology
(Co-Chair and author Block 3)
Irene Ridge, Department of Biological Sciences, Faculty of Science (Block 2)
Jonathan Silvertown, Department of Biological Sciences, Faculty of Science
(Chair and author Block 2)
Sandrine Simon, Systems Department, Faculty of Technology
(Chair and author Block 4)
Joe Smith, Department of Geography, Faculty of Social Science (Co-Chair and author Block 3)

Web and Multimedia Producer

Gloria Medina, Faculty of Science

Software Development

Phil Butcher, Learning and Teaching Solutions (CD-ROM development)
Sophia Braybrooke, Learning and Teaching Solutions (CD-ROM development)
Andrea Goodinson, Learning and Teaching Solutions (Web development)
Jason Jarratt, Learning and Teaching Solutions (CD-ROM development)
Ross Mackenzie, Learning and Teaching Solutions (Web development)
Gloria Medina, Faculty of Science (Software Production Manager and academic liaison)
Trent Williams, Learning and Teaching Solutions (Web development)
Damion Young, Learning and Teaching Solutions (CD-ROM and Web development)

Editors

Sheila Dunleavy
Ian Nuttall
Bina Sharma
Dick Sharp

Graphic Design

Sue Dobson
Carl Gibbard
David Winter

BBC/OU Production Centre

Sue Nuttall (Video for CD-ROM)

Other Contributors

Gary Alexander, Department of Telematics, Faculty of Technology (Block 4)
John Baxter, Faculty of Science (Community Interactions)
Roger Blackmore, Faculty of Technology (Day School, Project, activities for Block 1)
Gloria Medina (activities for Blocks 1 to 4)
Richard Treves, Faculty of Technology (Block 1)

Consultants

Claire Appleby, Open University Associate Lecturer (Block 4)
Hilary Denny, Open University Associate Lecturer
(Associate Lecturer recruitment, training and support)
Sarah Hardy (ECA)
Alex Kirby, BBC News Online environment correspondent (activities for Block 3)
Bob MacQueen, Open University Associate Lecturer (Reader)
Steve Millar, Open University Associate Lecturer (Reader)
Donal O'Donnell, Open University Associate Lecturer (Reader)
Julian Priddle, Science Teaching and Education Partnership (Block 1)

External Assessors

Professor Sandy Crosbie, Faculty of Science and Engineering,
University of Edinburgh (Course Assessor)
Dr Christopher Hope, Judge Institute of Management Studies, University of Cambridge (Block 3)
Dr John Shears, British Antarctic Survey, Cambridge (Block 1)
Mr David Streeter, School of Biological Sciences, University of Sussex (Block 2)
Dr Caroline Sullivan, Centre for Ecology and Hydrology at Wallingford, Oxfordshire (Block 4)

Contents

Chapter 1 A living world

Prepared for the course team by Jonathan Silvertown

1.1 Biting the apple

Bite an apple, enjoy the crunch and savour its fruity sweetness. As the juice trickles from the apple and onto your fingers, consider how this fruit arrived in your hand. In all likelihood you bought it in a supermarket where apples can be purchased all the year round. In late spring and summer they will come from the southern hemisphere, from South Africa, Chile and New Zealand. In autumn the apples on offer may come from Britain or France, but they could just as easily have been imported from the USA. The market in apples is a global one, but not all varieties are suited to international trade. A large supermarket might offer half-a-dozen varieties of apple, but this is a tiny fraction of the varieties that can be grown (Figure 1.1). Park Fruit Farm in Essex, for example, grows and sells 40 varieties. The National Fruit Collection at Brogdale in Kent grows 2300.

Among the first varieties to ripen in the orchard at Park Fruit Farm is Beauty of Bath, an apple with a pink-blushed yellow skin and an acid-sweet flavour. Like all the early-maturing varieties this apple keeps for only a few days after picking and will never be found in supermarkets. Slightly later comes the sweet, faintly strawberry-flavoured Discovery, which was first raised at another orchard in Essex from a cross between Beauty of Bath and Worcester Permain. Later arrivals in the farm shop have more familiar names because these varieties keep long enough to reach supermarkets: Cox's Orange Pippin, Bramley cooking apples and Gala. Apple names are like a poem celebrating apple-people, apple-places and apple-properties: the people who raised new varieties, the places where they originated, and the properties that make them distinctive:

Beauty of Kent, Bascombe Mystery
Ida Red, and Gloria Mundi
Ontario, Monarch, Queen and Knave
Delicious, Bountiful and George Cave
Ingrid Marie and Ross Nonpareil
Virginia Winsap, Reinette Rouge Etoilée
Edward the Seventh, King George the Fifth
Roundway Magnum Bonum, Granny Smith
Sheep's Nose, Hog's Snout, Bloody Butcher
Iron Pin, Curl Tail, Merton Worcester
Tom Putt, Fortune, Encore, Elan
Yorkshire Greening, Jester, Jonathan

Poetic and steeped in a sense of place they may be, yet apple names represent something much more than just a slice of horticultural history. Apple varieties represent an every-day encounter with **biodiversity**. At its simplest, the term biodiversity means the number of kinds of living things in a particular environment. Thus apple biodiversity in an orchard is represented by the number of distinct varieties present. In a natural environment, the number of *species* would be counted.

Local apple biodiversity is threatened by the dominance of just a few varieties in global trade, which makes orchards that grow and sell as many varieties as Park Fruit Farm

Figure 1.1 A selection of some apple varieties.

increasingly rare. More worryingly, large numbers of wild species of animal and plant, particularly those with only small, localized populations, are also endangered, as you will see in Section 1.3. Many environmentalists fear that we face a future world totally dominated by our *Homo sapiens* and a handful of cosmopolitan plants and animals forming global communities that lack any local distinctiveness. This would be the ultimate in globalization.

Biodiversity also has a broader, more all-encompassing definition that was given when the term was first coined at a scientific meeting in Washington DC in 1986. At the root of the broad concept of biodiversity is the notion that organisms differ genetically from one another and that life is hierarchically organized. Hence biodiversity is:

> … all hereditarily based variation at all levels of organization, from the *genes* within a single local *population* or *species*, to the species composing all or part of a local *community*, and finally to the communities themselves that compose the living parts of the multifarious *ecosystems* of the world.

(Wilson, 1997, emphasis added)

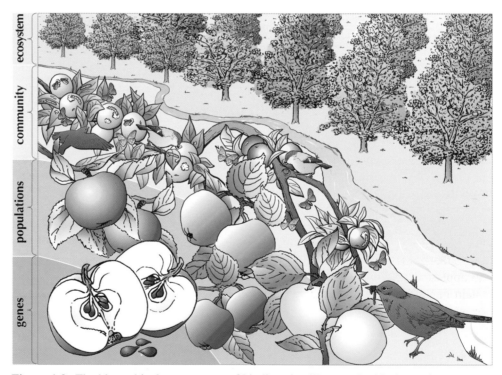

Figure 1.2 The hierarchical components of biodiversity, illustrated with the apple.

We shall explore the different levels of the concept of biodiversity (Figure 1.2), starting from the apple in your hand. Bite through to the core and you will find the pips. Each pip is a seed containing an embryo tree, with half its genes derived from the maternal tree (that produced the apple) and half derived from the pollen of another tree (the embryo's father). Flowers of most apple varieties require fertilization by pollen from a genetically *different* individual for successful fruit set. Apple trees belonging to the same variety are normally genetically identical with one another, so orchards must grow at least two varieties to achieve successful cross-fertilization.

⬤ Why are trees that belong to the same variety normally genetically identical?

● Apple varieties are propagated by grafting a scion (cutting) from a tree of the desired variety onto a rootstock. Since every scion has the genetic constitution of the tree from which it was taken, this ensures that the upper, fruiting part of the new tree is an identical copy of the original variety and bears the same kind of apple.

Genetically identical copies are called **clones**. The term **clone** is also used to refer to the entire collection of copies. There are millions of Granny Smith apple trees, grown in the temperate regions of both hemispheres, and all belong to one huge clone. When you grasp a Granny Smith, you are holding a part of one of the biggest organisms on Earth!

● If apple trees require cross-fertilization between varieties in order to bear fruit, why aren't the fruit hybrids?

● The flesh of the apple contains only the genes of the maternal tree, and these determine what the fruit looks and tastes like. However, the seeds inside the apple would produce hybrid fruit if grown to maturity.

Apples raised from seed display a great range of genetic variation for all kinds of properties, including the keeping qualities and flavour of their fruits. If apples that taste of pineapple, melon or banana sound like monstrosities or 'Frankenstein food' to you, think again. The varieties of apple at Brogdale that have these flavours are not the manufactures of a laboratory or of genetic engineering, but the products of traditional horticulture moulded from the raw material of genetic variation that resides wherever more than a single variety of apple is grown. We shall see later in this chapter just why such genetic resources are a valuable component of biodiversity.

Why do apple trees produce large, edible fruit? Part of the answer must be that generations of gardeners have used the genetic variation present in wild and cultivated **populations** of apple trees to hybridize and select trees with more and bigger fruit. Hence apple names such as Kentish Fillbasket and Eady's Magnum that proud gardeners have conferred on their prolific or extra-sized creations. But, where on Earth were, or where are (if they still exist), the ancestral populations of apples? It has long been thought that domesticated apples (*Malus domestica*) must descend from European wild crab apples, with which they readily hybridize. While some European varieties do contain genes from this source, the origin of the domesticated apple may be much more interesting than this.

In 1998, Barrie Juniper, a botanist from Oxford University, and colleagues went in search of wild populations of the apple that might be the ancestors of our modern varieties. They travelled to the Tien Shan mountains of central Asia on the remote border between China and Kazakhstan (Figure 1.3, *overleaf*):

> …we arrived, somewhat bruised and emotionally drained, at the lower mountain slopes of the Djungarian Alatau, an outlier of the great Tien Shan range (the Heavenly Mountains), just north of the Ili river and looking into China. In the morning as we emerged from our very comfortable yurt, we realized that we were surrounded by fruit forest of which the world knows very little. Apples, pears, plums, apricots, with other berrying trees such as hawthorns and rowans abound. Tiny fragments of this forest still exist, preserved by accident of political and military whim that has kept all but the most suicidal travellers out since the world began. And there we found

apple trees bearing fruit that to all intents and purposes resembled a cultivated apple. We returned to Oxford loaded with specimens for molecular biological analysis.

(Juniper, 2000, p. 29)

Figure 1.3 The location of the fruit forest (Tien Shan) visited by botanists from Oxford in 1998.

Back in Oxford, genetic analysis of apples collected from the fruit forest showed that these were indeed more closely related to domesticated apple varieties than those varieties are to the European crab apple. At some point, certainly more than 2000 years ago and maybe long before that, apples from the Tien Shan were taken westwards along the Silk Road to Europe. The Romans brought the descendants of these apples to Britain and grafted them onto rootstocks of the native crab apple. The variety known as Court Pendu Plat, still grown at Brogdale, may possibly be a Roman introduction.

No one knows exactly how wild apple trees in Tien Shan evolved fruit that would not look out of place in Marks and Spencer. One possibility might be that the human inhabitants of the Tien Shan selected and cultivated them and that the fruit forest is really a very ancient wild orchard. Equally possible is that animals in the fruit forest community favoured larger fruit, and that evolution by natural selection did the job. Essential to this argument is the fact that all fruit, whether rose hips or apples, aid the propagation of a plant's genes by attracting animals that will carry off their seeds. The biological function of fruit is seed dispersal, and this is why fruits contain sugars, fats and flavours that animals, including humans, find palatable. If you doubt this works as a means of gene propagation, consult Granny Smith.

Barrie Juniper imagined how the animal community might have influenced fruit evolution in the Tien Shan:

The original *Malus*, judging by the more than 20 wild species in central and southern China, bore a small fruit with hard but edible seeds, not dissimilar to those of the rowan tree (*Sorbus*) to which it is closely related, that were spread by birds…

According to this scenario, birds transported seeds of these ancestors of the apple into the Ili valley, where…

> …our neo-apple found a Shangri-La. Forest deer, wild pig and bears began to occupy the growing and rising woodland. Out of the steppe land, as it rose out of the Tethys Sea, moved great herds of wild horses and donkeys and perhaps camels. All of the herbivores would have gorged on the autumn harvests of wild fruit, selecting the larger, sweeter and juicier examples. Starting from the eastern tip of the Ili valley, our little apple expanded westwards, growing steadily larger as it moved, and changing, under evolutionary pressure, from a 'bird' fruit with edible seeds, to a 'mammal' fruit with poisonous seeds (apple pips contain cyanide). The seed coat, now smooth, black and hard, and shaped like a raindrop, evolved as a device more readily able to pass unharmed through animals' guts.

Bears still inhabit the fruit forest and gorge on apples before their winter hibernation. Bear dung in the forest sprouts apple seedlings as dense as mustard-and-cress.

Barrie Juniper tells a good story that may well be true. Whether or not he is right about how wild apples evolved large fruit, the interactions between wild fruit trees and the community of animals living with them is consistent with modern observations, so far as they go. We certainly have many instances of organisms evolving in response to the other species in the community. Some examples will be met later in this chapter. However, one problem is that there are almost no habitats left that have a completely intact community of large herbivores where the evolution of fruit can be investigated. In South America, for example, a whole fauna of large herbivores went extinct at around the time humans reached that continent – a pattern that has been repeated so often elsewhere as to constitute a very conspicuous smoking gun in the hands of *Homo sapiens*.

Bears are long extinct in Britain, though it is amusing to imagine them browsing a modern Kentish fruit forest. Since beavers may be re-introduced to Scotland, why not bears in the Home Counties? Less fancifully, the apple orchards of Kent do contain a community of species on which apple production depends.

- Which other species must be present in the community for the trees in an apple orchard to set fruit?
- Pollinating insects, usually honeybees, are required to transfer pollen between varieties.

The community also contains herbivores, such as codling moth caterpillars, bullfinches and aphids, carnivores, such as spiders and tits, which feed on insects, and pathogens, such as brown rot (Figure 1.4). There is also a rich community of organisms in the soil, including bacteria, fungi, earthworms, woodlice and other invertebrate animals that mainly consume dead organic matter, such as fallen leaves.

Figure 1.4 Some of the organisms associated with apple trees.

The trees in an orchard, the community of other species that live with them, and their non-living physical environment, are an **ecosystem**. Think of an ecosystem as a community plus its physical environment (Book 1, Section 2.1). It can be any size from a puddle to a prairie to a planet. Fundamental to the concept of an ecosystem is the idea that its parts are *connected* by the transfer of carbon and other chemical elements (particularly nitrogen (N), potassium (K) and phosphorus (P)) between them.

● How are earthworms and honeybees connected with apple trees in an orchard ecosystem?

● Earthworms live on organic matter in soil, which derives from dead leaves, whereas honeybees collect nectar from apple blossom. Dead leaves and nectar are carbon (or energy) sources for their respective consumers.

Ecosystems are rarely if ever self-contained and usually exchange materials with other ecosystems. For this reason, it is sometimes difficult to place a clear boundary around them. All terrestrial and most marine ecosystems exchange carbon dioxide with the atmosphere, so in a sense the entire planet can be considered one large ecosystem. We shall explore the global carbon cycle in Section 1.4.2.

1.2 Biodiversity and ecosystems: the environmental issues

The relationship between humans and nature is central to all environmental issues. The diversity of apple varieties that were once commercially cultivated demonstrates that human activities and biodiversity need not be antithetical, but the global dominance of just a few varieties today is a good example of the threat that globalization now poses to many aspects of biodiversity. The emergence of biodiversity as a global environmental issue is described by E. O. Wilson in his autobiography:

> The forum [in Washington DC] was the first occasion on which the word "biodiversity" was used, and after the publication of the book it spread with astonishing speed around the world: by 1987 it was one of the most frequently used terms in conservation literature. It became a favorite subject of museum exhibitions and college seminars. By June 1992, when more than a hundred heads of state met at the Earth Summit in Rio de Janeiro to debate and ratify global protocols on the environment, "biodiversity" approached the status of a household word. President Bush's refusal to sign the Convention on Biological Diversity on behalf of the United States brought the subject into the political mainstream….. Biodiversity, the concept, has become the talisman of conservation, embracing every kind of living creature.

> (Wilson, 1994)

Like an apple, the biodiversity issue can be cut in many ways. Here we shall attempt a brief overview of different perspectives before we look at the scale of the problem (Section 1.3), some of its consequences and some possible solutions (the remainder of Chapter 1 and Chapters 2 and 3).

1.2.1 Why does biodiversity matter?

The fundamental question is 'Why does biodiversity matter?' For most of us, this is usually a question of why it matters to human beings. Some environmental philosophers have given a great deal of time to whether we can argue that the non-human natural world has an intrinsic value, independent of humans. But after a few decades they are still in the depth of debate. We should leave it to them, and for now simply note that while biodiversity is of practical use to humans in very immediate ways (often expressed in economic terms), we also value biodiversity for aesthetic and ethical reasons. One might crudely summarize these reasons for preserving biodiversity as:

- Usefulness: 'Because we need it'
- Aesthetic: 'Because I like it'
- Ethical: 'Because it exists'

Liberty Hyde Bailey , an eminent horticulturist of the early 20th century, answered the question of why apple biodiversity matters from a personal perspective in his book *The Apple Tree*:

> Why do we need so many kinds of apples? Because there are so many folks. A person has a right to gratify his legitimate tastes. If he wants twenty or forty kinds of apples for his personal use, running from Early Harvest to Roxbury Russet, he should be accorded the privilege. Some place should be provided where he may obtain trees or scions. There is merit in variety itself. It provides more points of contact with life, and leads away from uniformity and monotony.
>
> (Bailey, 1922)

- Summarize Bailey's defence of apple biodiversity in terms of its value to people.
- Bailey takes for granted that apples are useful, but he also asserts the moral right of people to choose variety, and he believes that variety is desirable in its own right.

Most of us probably value biodiversity for a mixture of reasons, including the fact that it is economically useful to us, because it nourishes or clothes us, or because it simply pleases us in some way. It might please us because it is beautiful, or simply because it's 'there' and always will be – or, as many environmentalists state, 'should be'. Indeed, Bailey's numerous 'folks' need to include future generations. They are a common feature of discussions about global environmental changes, such as biodiversity loss and climate change. Earlier parts of the course touched on environmental values, and how these translate quickly into debates about obligations, for example to future generations. It can be difficult to separate out ethical economic and aesthetic ways of valuing nature, particularly when you take the view that humanity is a part of nature, not separate from it. This view is self-evident from an evolutionary and biological perspective, but human activities now so dominate the planet that it is difficult to deny that humans have set themselves apart to the extent that they could be said to be conducting a war upon the rest of nature. At times this war has been openly declared, as when the Chinese revolutionary leader Mao Zedong proclaimed that 'man must conquer nature', enacting an upheaval that led to famine and other disastrous results for China's land and people (Shapiro, 2001). Though he used 1960's sexist terminology, E. F. Schumacher summed up the irony of the relationship between humanity and nature rather well:

> Modern man does not experience himself as a part of nature, but as an outside force destined to dominate and conquer it. He even talks of a battle with nature, forgetting that, if he won the battle, he would find himself on the losing side.
>
> (Schumacher, 1973)

Schumacher's message was that we have to work with nature, not against it. For some this is a moral imperative, reinforced by the fact that humans are responsible for the damage done to the environment, but for others it is simply practical common sense.

1.2.2 The utility of biodiversity and ecosystems

In U316 we concentrate on why biodiversity matters from a practical perspective. This is not to say that these chapters don't relate thinking about the evident usefulness of biodiversity to ethical or aesthetic discussions of biodiversity's value. Indeed, it is often difficult to prise these apart: one person's aesthetic or ethical motivation for conserving biodiversity can create economic or political incentives for others to follow suit simply out of practical self-interest.

○ Recall an example of this from Book 1, Chapter 6.

● Eco-tourism is a clear example. The eco-tourist industry makes money because many people are willing and able to pay to exercise their aesthetic appreciation of nature. If the industry is to be sustainable, it must help to conserve the ecosystems that people wish to visit (and possibly to limit their numbers).

The idea that ecosystems and the species in them have an economic value is often encapsulated with the phrase **ecosystem services**. This term is at once banal and profound. Its truth is as banal as the observation that all life needs water. Its meaning is as profound as the intricate ways in which organisms in ecosystems process water, purifying it, harbouring it, consuming, recycling and even, in the case of plants, splitting it to generate breathable oxygen. The processing of water is a particularly good example of a service provided by an ecosystem, and one that is discussed in *World Resources* (*WR*) and Book 4. Another is the role of ecosystems in the carbon cycle, which we shall examine later in this chapter, and which is central to the issue of global climate change, discussed in Book 3.

Ecosystem services tend to be taken for granted until they fail because the ecosystem has been altered in some way, and then the cost has to be counted. Ecosystem services are simply natural ecosystem processes that someone has consciously put a value on. It is useful to distinguish between two different roles for biodiversity that are hidden within the idea of ecosystem services. The first is that species play vital roles in the functioning of ecosystems. Plants and algae capture the energy of sunlight, using this to fuel the manufacture of cells, leaves and wood that feed the rest of the community. Without plants or marine algae, most ecosystems on Earth would cease to function. We will look at the role of different species in ecosystem functioning in Section 1.5.

The second role for biodiversity in ecosystem services is the direct economic benefit to humans that can be derived from biodiversity products such as the timber harvested from forests or the fish harvested from the ocean. This will be examined in Section 1.4. However, before we can investigate these matters, we first need to know what we have and what is happening to it. *WR* addresses this question for whole ecosystems, and here we ask the same question for organisms – the living component of ecosystems.

1.3 Species and extinction

1.3.1 What is a species?

To catalogue living things we must first describe and name them. Biodiversity is the product of evolution from a single origin of life on Earth, which took place around 3.5–4.0 billion years ago. How life originated from non-living molecules is a fascinating, and so-far unanswered, question. Because of a fundamental similarity of structure and biochemistry shared by all living things, we can be fairly sure that this occurred successfully only once.

Though species are not the only unit by which biodiversity may be measured, the species is arguably the most natural because it is the only one defined by the existence of a genetic barrier. According to this definition, known as the **biological species concept**, a species is the collection of all individuals that may potentially breed with one another to produce fertile offspring. A biological species is said to be **reproductively isolated** from other species because it cannot interbreed with them to produce fertile offspring. For example, donkeys and horses belong to different species because their hybrid, the mule, is sterile and cannot itself breed. In practice, it is rarely if ever possible to test whether individuals belong to the same species by experimentally crossing them. Fossil species clearly cannot be defined by any such criterion, and what palaeontologists and biologists look for instead are discontinuities in structure or (if the species is living) behaviour or physiology that suggest two populations are in fact different enough to be considered distinct species.

Although the biological species concept, if pragmatically interpreted, is useful for animals, plants and fungi, it is not so useful for describing the biodiversity of microbes, such as bacteria. Bacteria break the rules because genes can be transferred between different bacterial species: this is how characteristics such as drug-resistance may spread. Therefore, particularly in bacteria, any meaningful measure of biodiversity must include not just the organisms themselves, but the genes too.

The description and classification of living things into groups is the science of **taxonomy** (Box 1.1, on p. 18).

1.3.2 Species: how many and where?

About 1.4–1.7 million living species have been described and named, but it is variously estimated that there may be anywhere between 2 million and 80 million in total. The consensus view seems to be about 10 million. The numbers of known species are not evenly distributed across the globe, but are concentrated in particular regions (Figure 1.5, *overleaf*).

- Compare the distribution of biodiversity shown for animals and plants combined in Figure 1.5 with the map of plant biodiversity shown in Figure 1.6. What are the major similarities and differences between the two maps?

- Note first that Figure 1.5 maps biodiversity within country boundaries whereas Figure 1.6 ignores these. Both maps show that biodiversity is greatest in tropical countries/areas, with certain places outside the tropics, such as South Africa and China, also having high biodiversity. A large difference between the two maps is that Figure 1.6 shows that plant biodiversity is not uniformly high within the high-diversity countries identified by Figure 1.5. For example, high plant biodiversity in South Africa occurs mainly in the Cape region, and in South America it is particularly high along the Andes.

● Compare the distribution of biodiversity shown for freshwater fishes in Figure 1.7 with the map of plant biodiversity shown in Figure 1.6. What are the major similarities and differences between the two maps?

● Both maps show biodiversity to be most concentrated within the tropics, but at a more detailed geographical level the maps are very different. In South America, fish biodiversity is greatest in the Amazon basin and lower in the Andes where plant biodiversity is highest. Similarly, fish biodiversity in Africa is highest in Central Africa, whereas plants are most diverse to the west, east and far south of this area.

Norman Myers and co-authors (2000) from Conservation International have estimated that 35% of the species of land vertebrates (mammals, birds, reptiles and amphibians) and 44% of plants are to be found in just 1.4% of the land surface of the Earth.

● What is the practical implication of this distribution of known species?

● It suggests that concentrating conservation efforts on such biodiversity 'hotspots' could be an effective way to safeguard a disproportionately large number of species.

We shall consider this concentration of species into hotspots in greater depth later in the book.

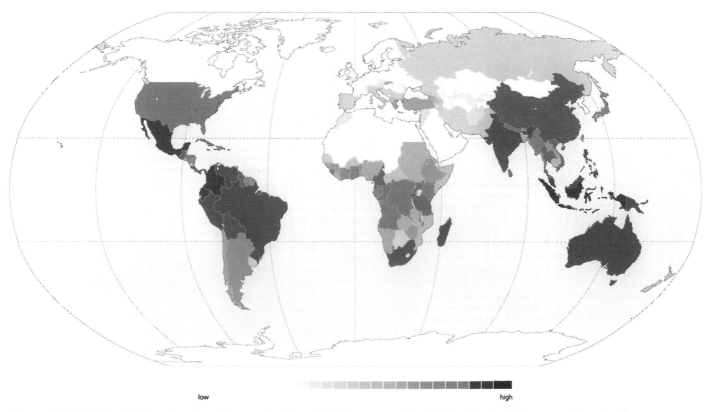

low   high

Figure 1.5 Relative biodiversity of vertebrate animals and plants at country level, allowing for differences in land surface area between countries.

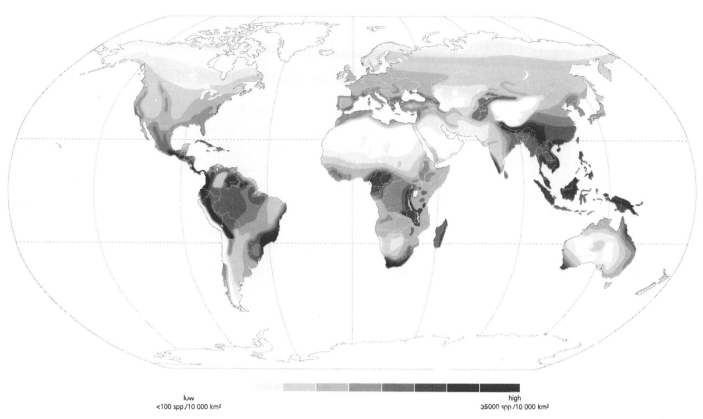

<100 spp./10 000 km²

high
≥5000 spp./10 000 km²

Figure 1.6 Biodiversity in numbers of known plant species per 10 000 km² of land surface area.

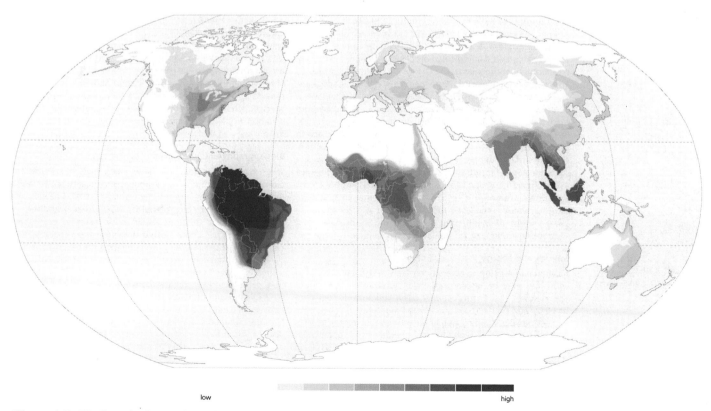

low

high

Figure 1.7 Biodiversity in numbers of known freshwater fish families per 10 000 km² of land surface area.

Box 1.1 Taxonomy: names and the genealogy of living things

Modern taxonomy has its origins in the work of the 18th century Swedish naturalist Carl Linnaeus. He catalogued all species then known to Western science in a hierarchical system, placing them into two kingdoms (plants and animals), and within these into further sub-divisions down to genus and species. Today, we recognize three **domains** (the most fundamental groups of living things) and eight **kingdoms** (Figure 1.8). Organisms in two of the domains, **Bacteria** (also called Eubacteria) and **Archaea**, are mostly one-celled microbes of great diversity. Though so easy to overlook because of their microscopic size, these microbes are of enormous ecological importance in all ecosystems. The third domain, **Eukarya**, contains four kingdoms: **Plantae**, **Animalia**, **Fungi** and the rest, which are mainly one-celled organisms (such as *Amoeba* and single-celled algae) called **Protoctista**.

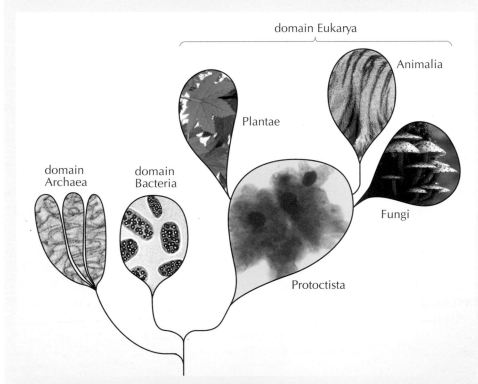

Figure 1.8 The probable relationship between the three domains of life.

All known species that have been formally described by a taxonomist are still named in the Linnean style by a binomial, usually in Latin, consisting of the name of the genus to which the species belongs followed by the species name (or epithet). Humans belong to the genus *Homo* and the species *sapiens* (literally 'intelligent human'). The scientific name of the English oak is *Quercus robur* (literally 'strong oak'), and so on. Note that a capital letter is given to the name of the genus (*Homo*, *Quercus*) but not to the specific epithet (*sapiens, robur*) and that the genus and species names are written in italic or underlined.

Linnaeus, like the great majority of naturalists until Darwin's publication of *The Origin of Species* in 1859, believed that species were each separately created by God and that the underlying order in their variety which made it possible to classify them indicated how the deity had designed creation. Darwin's big breakthrough was twofold. First, he realized that the variation that can be seen *within* most species implies that species are not fixed entities, and second he came up with a mechanism, known as **natural selection**, which could explain how inherited variation within species could lead to the evolution of new species. Huge strides in our understanding of the details of evolution and the history of life have been made since Darwin's day, but his evolutionary world-view remains the framework of all modern biology. The most fundamental change that has occurred in evolutionary studies since Darwin is in our understanding of **genetics**, or how inheritance works. Although the inheritance of variation is central to Darwin's theory of evolution by natural selection, he did not understand the mechanism of inheritance as we do today.

1.3.3 Extinction

The fossil record is imperfect, but it suggests that the majority of species that have ever lived are extinct. Even whole groups, such as the dinosaurs and the ammonites, which were once both diverse and numerous are now entirely gone. Five episodes of 'mass extinction' during the history of life are known and in the greatest of them, at the end of the Permian Era about 248 million years ago, it has been estimated that as many as 95% of animal species then living became extinct. Some extinct groups do have modern descendants — for example, one dinosaur group gave rise to the birds, of which nearly 10 000 species have been recognized and named. Thus, the extinction of some species and the evolution of new ones are natural processes. The cause for concern today is not the *fact* of extinction, but rather the *rate* at which it is now occurring, which appears to be far from normal. As E. O. Wilson has put it '…virtually all students of the extinction process agree that biological diversity is in the midst of its sixth great crisis, this time precipitated entirely by man.'

Extinction rates are expressed in units of the number (or percentage) of extinctions per species per year. Thus, to calculate an extinction rate for fossil or living species we need an estimate of (i) the number of species present to start with and (ii) the number becoming extinct over an interval of time. None of these quantities can be calculated with exactitude, either in the fossil record or in the present day, but they can be estimated in a variety of ways. Estimates from the fossil record show that extinction rates over geological time varied continuously, even between periods of mass extinction, but the generally accepted average rate over the last 600 million years is one extinction per million species per year.

- What is one in a million expressed as a percentage extinction rate?

- $1/1 000 000$ is 10^{-6}, and to convert this into a percentage we multiply by a hundred $(100 - 10^2)$ This gives $10^{-6} \times 10^2 = 10^{-4}$, or 0.0001% of species per year.

This is the generally accepted **background extinction rate** for the pre-human era and the value against which modern extinction rates need to be judged. The World Conservation Monitoring Centre, an agency of the United Nations Environment Programme (UNEP), gathers statistics on global biodiversity (e.g. the maps in Figures 1.5–1.7) and has compiled a list of extinctions that are known to have occurred since AD 1600 (Table 1.1). The data are expressed as a percentage for the whole 400-year period, rather than per year.

Table 1.1 Threatened and extinct species.

	Number of known species in group	Approximate proportion of group assessed	Threatened species	% of total in group threatened	Extinct species	% of total in group extinct since AD 1600
Vertebrates						
Mammals	4630	100%	1096	24%	88	2%
Birds	9946	100%	1107	11%	107	1%
Reptiles	7400	<15%	253	3%	20	0.3%
Amphibians	4950	<15%	124	3%	5	0.1%
Fishes	25 000	<10%	734	3%	172	0.7%
Invertebrates						
Insects	950 000	<0.01%	537	0.05%*	73	0.004%
Molluscs	70 000	<5%	920	1%	237	0.3%
Crustaceans	40 000	<5%	407	1%	10	0.03%
Others			27		4	
Plants (Ferns, conifers and flowering plants)	270 000	<20%	30 827	11%	>400	0.2%

* Note that this value is five times the proportion actually assessed (shown in column 3). This impossible result is not a typographical error, but rather reflects the fact that the two percentages were calculated from two different sources that have not be reconciled with one another. It is an example of what can happen to estimates when a group is as little known as the insects, making uncertainties very large.

- What is the expected background extinction rate for 400 years?

- $400 \times 0.0001\% = 0.04\%$ of species expected to go extinct between AD 1600 and AD 2000.

- How do the extinction rates shown in Table 1.1 compare with the background rate?

- All the extinction rates, except those for insects (0.004%), crustaceans (0.03%) and amphibians (0.1%) are at least five times greater than the background rate (0.04%).

- What relationship is there (if any) between the estimated extinction rates for groups and the approximate proportion of the group that has been assessed?

- The estimates are much higher for groups that have been comprehensively assessed (mammals and birds) than for poorly studied groups.

It is not easy to become a recognized member of the extinct species club. To qualify for inclusion in the extinction counts in Table 1.1 the rule is that the death of the last known individual must be beyond reasonable doubt. For example, the extinction of the passenger pigeon occurred when the last bird died in captivity; the Tasmanian wolf (thylacine) is considered extinct because it has not been seen since 1936. Because it is so much easier to prove existence (sighting of one individual of a species is all that is needed) than extinction, the extinction statistics must greatly underestimate the true extinction rate. This is borne out by the positive correlation between how well groups are known and extinction rates. Where they are most reliable, the statistics show that extinctions are at least 50 times greater than the background rate in mammals and 25 times greater in birds. In groups with numerous undescribed species, such as the insects, extinctions must surely occur before the existence of some species has even been recognized.

With some exceptions, most of the known extinctions among mammals and birds have occurred on oceanic islands. The dodo of Mauritius is the most famous example (Book 1). Mammal extinctions include two marine species, the Caribbean monk seal and Steller's sea cow, but no whales. Does this mean that worries about species extinction on a massive scale on continents are exaggerated? Humans in historical times have so far extinguished a few percent of mammals and birds, but the end-Permian extinction saw 95% extinction rates among marine animals in the fossil record. Are comparisons between what is happening now and the mass extinctions of the past a gross exaggeration? Bjorn Lomborg (2001) has argued in his book *The Skeptical Environmentalist* that extinction rates are about 0.7% per 50 years (0.014% per year), or approximately 140 times the background rate: high, but not massive. Others have argued that the true figure is nearer 10 or even a 100 times this. Lomborg's figure appears to be lower than, for example, E. O. Wilson's, because Lomborg ignored the unsustainability of small populations.

A population is said to be **sustainable** if it is not threatened with extinction in the foreseeable future, but what do *sustainable*, *threat* and *foreseeable future* mean in quantitative terms? For conservation purposes, the International Union for the Conservation of Nature and Natural Resources (IUCN) uses a time horizon of 100 years for what is foreseeable, and recognizes that the threat of extinction is subject to chance. A population is considered threatened if there is a 10% *or greater* probability of extinction in 100 years. If the threat of extinction occurring is less than 10% in 100 years, the population should be at lower risk and may be sustainable. Note, however, that by this definition some 10% of species not recognized as threatened may still go extinct within 100 years. Also, among species where the 10% risk of extinction is exceeded, some have a much higher probability of extinction than just 10%. To allow for this, the category 'threatened' is divided by the IUCN into 'critically endangered' (at least a 50% probability of extinction in 10 years or three generations, whichever is the longer), 'endangered' (at least a 20% probability of extinction in 20 years or five generations, whichever is the longer) and 'vulnerable'.

In practice, a whole range of methods and tools is used by scientists who specialize in the study of particular groups of species to decide whether particular species should be classified as 'threatened', and if so how bad the threat is. In addition to numbers of individuals (where these can be estimated), criteria used to evaluate threat include the size of area that a species occupies and how fragmented this is. Downward trends in distribution or abundance are particularly important for detecting extinction threats, and populations that fluctuate in distribution or abundance are also considered to be at extra risk.

Estimating extinction risks for threatened species as a group is fraught with difficulty because, as described, the threatened species range from the critically endangered to the merely vulnerable. However, if we make the assumption that the last threatened species will finally go extinct in 100 years, then the extinction rates over a century are the percentages of threatened species shown in Table 1.1.

• If 24% of threatened species of mammals and 11% of birds in Table 1.1 were to go extinct in the next 100 years, how would these rates compare with that calculated by Lomborg (0.7% over 50 years)?

• The 50-year rates for mammals and birds would be, respectively, 24%/2 = 12% and 11%/2 = 5.5%, an order of magnitude greater than Lomborg's figure.

On the basis of known threats to described species, the per-year extinction rates for birds and mammals cover the range 0.11–0.24%, or one-to-two thousand times the background rate. Unfortunately, even this figure is probably highly conservative because there are good reasons to believe that the threats to some lesser-known groups of organisms are even greater than those to birds and mammals. The reason is that mammals and birds are subject to widespread conservation efforts that lower extinction risk. Groups such as freshwater molluscs have scarcely been evaluated for population sustainability at all and receive few targeted conservation measures. You will see in *WR* that freshwater habitats, where many threatened molluscs live, are especially vulnerable.

Now go to the Web and do the activities associated with this chapter.

1.4 Ecosystem functions

1.4.1 Water

Biodiversity plays numerous roles in the water cycle and in the processing of water. Over land, the local climate and rainfall are influenced by forest cover. In the Amazon basin, for example, the trees of the tropical forest return about half the rainfall back to the atmosphere by evapotranspiration through their leaves. Other estimates are that as little as one-third of the rain that falls on land comes directly from the oceans, and that the remainder comes from evaporation from land surfaces and evapotranspiration by plants. Computer models suggest that deforestation of large blocks of Amazon rainforest would reduce rainfall significantly, though since precipitation in the Amazon basin averages 2000 mm a year it would still have a wet climate.

The reason why trees are such efficient recyclers of water is that each square metre of ground in a broad-leaved forest may have above it 5–8 square metres of leaf surface. Every leaf is peppered with tiny pores called stomata through which water vapour escapes and where carbon dioxide and oxygen are exchanged with the atmosphere. Trees do not just move water between the soil and the air, but also transport it from deep in the soil to the surface. By a nocturnal process known as hydraulic lift, which has been discovered only relatively recently, trees pump water from depth to the surface, where some of it leaks out and is available to other plants. It has been calculated that a single large sugar maple tree, a native of north-eastern North America, lifts 100 litres of water per night during the growing season.

In drier geographical regions, vegetation may be so significant in influencing local climate that losing the plants can mean losing the rain. It has been estimated that in parts of West Africa that lie 1000 km from the southern coast virtually all the rain comes from local evapotranspiration and none from the distant ocean or from forests elsewhere. In this kind of environment, once precipitation has been reduced there may be no way back because there is insufficient water to support vegetation. It is possible that this is how parts of sub-Saharan Africa, where once there was healthy vegetation, became desert, although the case is not proven.

In hydrological terms, forests are like giant sponges or water reservoirs. The sponge does release water of course, but thanks to tree roots that bind the soil together and stop it being washed away, the streams that issue from forested watersheds are clear and not laden with silt. A muddy river is a sure sign that all is not well with the vegetation in its catchment. Not just trees, but perennial vegetation of any kind will bind soil with roots. Seasonal crops grown with farming practices that leave bare soil exposed at rainy times of year result in losses of soil that are huge on a global scale. As land loses its topsoil so its fertility and its ability to retain water decline. Humus, which helps to retain soil moisture, is largely contained in the surface layers of the soil, so that when they are washed away the remaining soil becomes even more prone to erosion. As a result, once erosion has begun it can become a runaway process that just gets worse and worse, ultimately making arable land completely useless for farming.

Water processing is not confined to terrestrial ecosystems. Aquatic ecosystems have their own suites of detritivores and decomposers that break down dead organic matter. In freshwater the aquatic equivalents of woodlice, which consume dead leaf material, are shrimps, which, like woodlice, are crustaceans. However, most of the smaller animals in freshwater are insects with aquatic larvae that develop into terrestrial, flying adults. Mosquitoes are a notorious example whose larvae and pupae are both aquatic inhabitants, mainly of still waters. Dragonflies have aquatic larvae that are voracious predators in streams and ponds. Molluscs, such as clams, mussels and oysters, are filter-feeders that remove microscopic particles and single-celled algae from the water column, thereby clarifying it. Over-fishing, pollution and other human activities have destroyed the estuarine oyster beds that once crowded the shores of Chesapeake Bay on the east coast of the USA, but it has been calculated that when the estuarine ecosystem was intact its oyster beds filtered the entire water column every three days.

1.4.2 The carbon cycle

Carbon dioxide (CO_2) produced by the burning of fossil fuels — oil, coal and natural gas — is believed to be responsible for a rise in the atmospheric concentration of this greenhouse gas from around 280 parts per million (p.p.m.) in pre-industrial times to nearly 380 p.p.m. at the beginning of the 21st century (Figure 1.9, *overleaf*). This has begun a process of global climate change with enormous environmental conseqences (Block 3). Fossil fuels are the buried carbon residues of organisms that lived in ancient ecosystems. Coal measures are the fossilized remains of trees that lived in swamps in the Upper Carboniferous, a period that ended about 290 million years ago. Oil and natural gas derive from marine organisms. These fuels are not renewable because the ecosystems that produced them no longer exist, but the CO_2 released by burning fossil fuels enters the modern carbon cycle through the atmosphere and from there it enters modern ecosystems.

It is the atmosphere that makes the carbon cycle truly global because it mixes gases so rapidly. However, the inputs of CO_2 to the atmosphere, and the outputs from it, are localized. Estimates of the amounts of carbon involved in the global cycle are shown in Figure 1.10 (p. 25). Study this Figure and then answer the following questions, but before you do so, acquaint yourself with the units used to measure masses of carbon, which are described in Box 1.2.

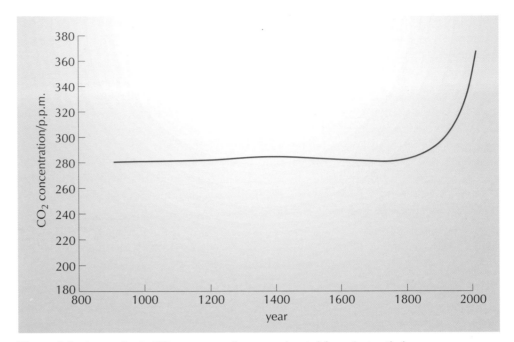

Figure 1.9 Atmospheric CO_2 concentrations as estimated from Antarctic ice cores (from AD 900 to AD 1990) and, more recently, as measured at the Mauna Loa observatory in Hawaii.

Box 1.2 Units of measurement for mass

The global carbon cycle involves some very large masses, and so the units used to measure them are unlikely to be familiar to you. However, the units are simply large multiples of smaller units, such as the gram.

Unit	Equivalent
gram (g)	1/1000th (or 10^{-3}) kg
kilogram (kg)	1000 (or 10^3) g
tonne (t)	10^3 kg (or 10^6 g)
gigatonne (Gt)	10^9 t (or 10^{12} kg)
petagram (Pg)	10^{15} g (or 10^{12} kg or 1 Gt)

Note that carbon budgets are shown in terms of masses of carbon rather than masses of carbon dioxide: 1 Gt C is equivalent to 3.7 Gt CO_2. This is because there is 1 gram of carbon in every 3.7 grams of carbon dioxide.

● Which are the main compartments in the natural carbon cycle shown in Figure 1.10a, and what are their relative capacities for carbon?

● There are four compartments: rocks, terrestrial ecosystems (mainly soil and plants), the atmosphere and the ocean. Excluding the carbon in rocks, the amount of which is unquantified, the compartment that contains the largest amount of carbon by far is the ocean (38 000 PgC). Next largest are terrestrial ecosystems (2000 PgC in total), particularly soil (1500 PgC), and the smallest compartment is the atmosphere (730 PgC).

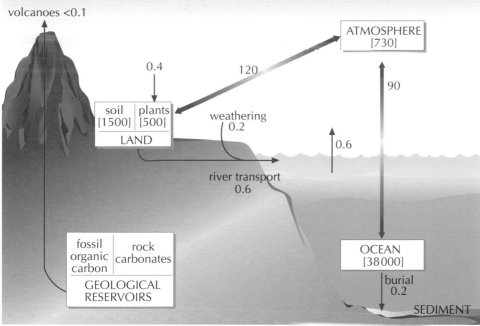

(a)

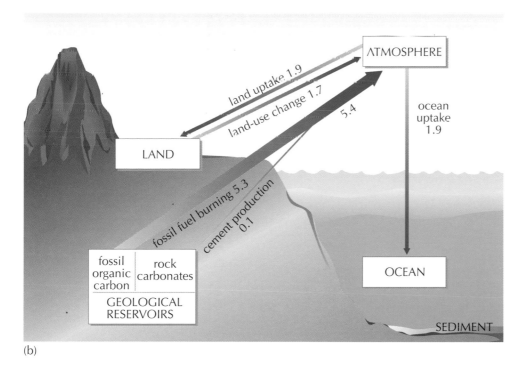

(b)

Figure 1.10 The global carbon budget, with reservoirs measured in PgC and fluxes in PgC yr^{-1}: (a) the natural system and its components; (b) anthropogenic sources of atmospheric CO_2 and the fate of the additional carbon. Double-headed arrows indicate that inputs and outputs are in balance.

● Do the annual carbon inputs and outputs from the atmosphere in the natural cycle balance?

● Yes. The double-headed arrows between the land and atmosphere and the ocean and atmosphere indicate equal amounts of carbon flowing in either direction.

An additional 0.4 PgC yr^{-1} is taken from the atmosphere by plants and 0.2 PgC yr^{-1} is removed by weathering. These amounts are transported to the ocean via rivers, and are balanced by the 0.6 PgC yr^{-1} that is returned from the oceans to the atmosphere.

○ What are the main anthropogenic sources of CO_2 and their sizes shown in Figure 1.10b?

● The main anthropogenic sources, in order of size, are: burning of fossil fuels (5.3 PgC yr^{-1}), land-use change (1.7 PgC yr^{-1}) and cement production (0.1 PgC yr^{-1}).

○ What happens to the carbon from anthropogenic sources? How much is unaccounted for?

● Oceans and land each take up 1.9 Pg of anthropogenic carbon each per year, or 3.8 PgC yr^{-1} in total. The total entering the atmosphere from anthropogenic sources is 7.1 PgC yr^{-1}, so 3.3 PgC yr^{-1} is unaccounted for.

○ What percentage of the atmospheric reservoir does the annual anthropogenic carbon not taken up by terrestrial ecosystems and oceans represent?

● The atmospheric reservoir is 730 PgC and the carbon not taken up each year is 3.3 PgC, which is $3.3/730 \times 100 = 0.48\%$, or about half of one percent.

The values shown in Figure 1.10 are estimates taken from the scientific report of the Intergovernmental Panel on Climate Change (IPCC) published in 2001 (Houghton *et al.*, 2001). Any estimate is, by definition, not an exact quantity but a measurement made with some degree of uncertainty or statistical 'error' (Book 1) over a particular period of time. The estimates in Figure 1.10 are for the 1980s. Uncertainties can themselves be quantified and comparisons can be made between different estimates to check that they are consistent. Houghton et al. (2001) estimated that, over the decade 1980–1989, the amount of carbon (as CO_2) in the atmosphere rose by 3.3 ± 0.1 PgC yr^{-1}. (During the 1990s the estimated rate was 3.2 ± 0.1 PgC yr^{-1}.)

○ Compare the 1980s estimate with your answer to the previous question based on the data in Figure 1.10b. Are the two estimates consistent?

● The data in Figure 1.10b indicated that 3.5 PgC yr^{-1} of anthropogenic carbon is not taken up by sinks on land or in the ocean. No estimate of the error attached to this figure was given, but it is very similar to the annual rise in atmospheric carbon in the 1980s, which was 3.3 ± 0.1 PgC yr^{-1}.

Organisms are responsible for the majority of natural transfers of carbon between land and atmosphere, and the ability of terrestrial ecosystems to mop up and store anthropogenic carbon depends on their biological activity. Transfers of carbon between the oceans and the atmosphere involve organisms less directly, because most marine plants and animals exchange dissolved CO_2 with seawater rather than with the air. (Marine mammals are air-breathing and the only exception.) The ocean contains a large reservoir of dissolved inorganic carbon, a good deal of it derived from biological activity.

Two biological processes are of fundamental importance to the carbon cycle. These are **aerobic respiration** and **photosynthesis**. All living organisms respire and the majority do so aerobically, which means they require oxygen. Aerobic respiration uses oxygen to turn carbohydrates (e.g. sugars) into carbon dioxide and water with the release of chemical energy. Chemically, respiration is identical with combustion, and like combustion it produces CO_2.

Photosynthesis, of which only plants, algae and certain bacteria are capable, is the chemical reverse of respiration. It uses the energy of sunlight to 'fix' CO_2 into soluble sugars and, in the process, water molecules are split and oxygen is released. Photosynthetic organisms do not depend on other organisms for their supply of carbon, and are described as **autotrophs** (literally 'self-feeders'). Photosynthesis is the key to ecosystems' ability to take up carbon, but how much is stored and how much is released again in respiration depends upon the organisms involved and on ecological conditions.

In some plants, the biochemical reactions involved in photosynthesis are sensitive to the atmospheric concentration of CO_2, and these plants may respond to an increase by growing better (up to 33% more growth for a doubling in CO_2 in some cases). This **CO_2 fertilization effect** results from indirect and as well as direct effects of CO_2 concentration on plant physiology. Because plants both gain CO_2 and lose water through the same pores in their leaves (the stomata), higher concentrations of CO_2 mean that less water is lost for each gram of carbon fixed. Thus, higher CO_2 concentrations can indirectly affect how plants use water. Nitrogen use can also be indirectly affected because a good deal of the nitrogen that a plant needs is used to manufacture the main enzyme involved in photosynthesis. This enzyme works more efficiently at higher CO_2 concentrations, so more carbon is fixed per gram of nitrogen in these conditions.

- How does CO_2 fertilization of plant growth complicate the response of ecosystems to increased concentrations of atmospheric CO_2?

- In at least three ways. First, because more CO_2 may be fixed by plants, but also because plant use of water and nitrogen may change as a consequence.

If photosynthesis is the key to an ecosystem's ability to take up carbon, the control of **decomposition** is the key to carbon storage. Decomposer organisms, for example the bacteria, fungi and invertebrate animals found in soil (see above) feed on the dead remains of other organisms. Organisms that, like animals and microbial decomposers, obtain carbon from other organisms are called **heterotrophs** (literally 'other-feeders').

Figure 1.11 (*overleaf*) summarizes the global amounts of carbon that are stored annually in various compartments of terrestrial ecosystems and the transfers (fluxes) between them and the atmosphere; values are in PgC yr^{-1}. The three main compartments are primary producers (autotrophic plants), detritus (dead and decomposing plant and animal matter) and soil. Other significant compartments are primary consumers (herbivores, such as caterpillars) and secondary consumers (carnivores, such as spiders). **Detritivores** are the invertebrate animals, such as woodlice, that eat detritus. **Decomposers** are the microbes, including bacteria, fungi and protoctists, that cause the breakdown of organic matter so that it becomes incorporated into the soil. Relatively little carbon is stored by heterotrophs, which include animals, fungi and bacteria, but these organisms are very important in the fluxes.

The carbon fixed by plants is called **gross primary production** (GPP), and that which is left after autotrophic respiration is termed **net primary production** (NPP). Study Figure 1.11, and then answer the following questions.

- What proportion of the carbon fixed by photosynthesis is respired by autotrophs?

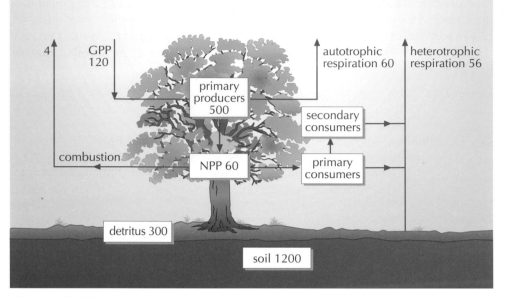

Figure 1.11 The main components of the carbon cycle on land.

● GPP is 120 PgC yr^{-1}, and NPP is exactly half this amount, so autotrophic respiration accounts for half the carbon fixed by photosynthesis.

● What happens to the carbon in NPP?

● Ultimately, nearly all of it is eaten and respired by heterotrophs (56 PgC yr^{-1}), with the remainder returning to the atmosphere from fires (4 PgC yr^{-1}).

Note that NPP is not all directly consumed and respired by animals and decomposers. Most of it will be stored for a time in wood, leaves and roots and then it may pass by various routes through primary and secondary consumers, detritus and decomposers before finally returning to the atmosphere as CO_2. The length of time it takes a carbon atom to pass through a compartment is called the **turnover time** (or residence time). Turnover time depends on the longevity of the organism and tissues of which the carbon is a part, and upon the activity of consumers and decomposers. Because, on a global average, about three-quarters of the carbon in terrestrial ecosystems is in the soil (Figure 1.10a), it is the detritivores and decomposers in this compartment, especially the bacteria, that mainly control how long it takes for a carbon atom that enters as NPP to leave in respired CO_2. The main factors controlling bacterial activity are temperature and oxygen availability. Ecosystems in cold climates or with waterlogged soils where oxygen is in low concentration have much longer turnover times for carbon than warmer environments where soils are moist and oxygenated.

Figure 1.12 shows the amounts of carbon stored at any one time (the 'stock') in different terrestrial ecosystem types. Study this figure and then answer the following question.

● Among tropical, temperate and boreal (far-northern) forests compare (i) the total carbon stocks and (ii) the relative distribution of carbon between plants and soil. What geographical patterns do the two comparisons show?

● The comparisons show different patterns: (i) total carbon stocks are in the order tropical > boreal > temperate; (ii) the ratios of carbon in plants and soil are in the order tropical > temperate > boreal.

Tropical forests contain the greatest stock of carbon because they cover a greater area than either of the other types of forest and because the plant component contains more carbon per hectare than in temperate or boreal forests. Boreal forests come next because they are more extensive than temperate forests and contain much more soil carbon per hectare than forests in either tropical or temperate regions.

● Suggest an explanation for the geographical pattern of variation in the plant to soil carbon ratio.

● The ratio changes with latitude and climate, with a greater proportion of total C present in the soil as you move from the tropics to the temperate zone to the boreal zone. The likeliest explanation for this is that the decomposition rate and the turnover rate of carbon in the soil are much lower in the cooler climates of the north than they are nearer the Equator.

● What patterns are present in the plant to soil carbon ratio when (i) tropical and temperate grasslands and (ii) the remaining ecosystem types shown in Figure 1.12 are compared? How may these patterns be explained?

● (i) A greater fraction of total carbon is present in the soil in temperate grasslands than in tropical grasslands. The pattern is the same as for the temperate/tropical forest comparison and probably has the same explanation. (ii) The four remaining ecosystems are all characterized by having nearly all the carbon in the soil compartment, but the reason is different in each case. In wetlands, lack of oxygen (anoxia) in the soil caused by waterlogging inhibits decomposition and causes carbon to accumulate; in arid lands, drought limits NPP and inhibits decomposition in the soil; in the tundra, the very short growing season and low temperatures have the same effects; in croplands, the plants are short-lived and are removed at harvest, which limits the accumulation of above-ground plant tissue.

The amounts of carbon stocks in different ecosystem types and the distribution of carbon between plants and soil give us some idea of how human actions that indirectly or directly affect ecosystems may alter the global carbon budget. For example, the estimated annual transfer of 1.7 PgC from terrestrial ecosystems to the atmosphere due

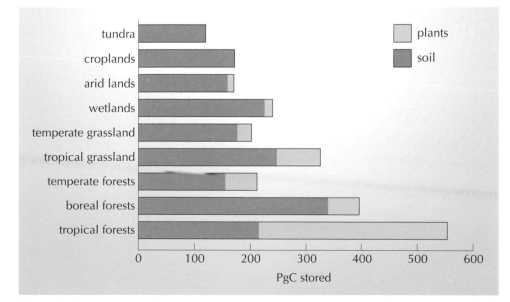

Figure 1.12 Terrestrial carbon stocks in soil and plants in various terrestrial ecosystems.

to land-use change in the 1980s (Figure 1.10b) was mainly due to tropical deforestation. The high plant to soil carbon ratio in tropical forests (Figure 1.12) explains why such a large effect on atmospheric inputs might be expected when tropical forest is replaced by grassland, which contains very little carbon above ground. Carbon below ground in grasslands takes time to build up.

- What effect would you expect global warming, which is expected to be greatest at high latitudes, to have on the carbon storage of boreal forest and tundra?

- Most of the carbon in these ecosystems is in the soil, where low temperatures limit its rate of release by decomposition. A rise in temperature could be expected to decrease the carbon turnover time and to result in an increase in CO_2 released to the atmosphere. Some of the stored carbon could also be released.

Organisms play a role in the marine as well as the terrestrial part of the global carbon cycle. There are some fundamental differences, however, the major one being that whereas terrestrial ecosystems store carbon largely in the undecomposed remains of organisms, the ocean stores carbon mainly in inorganic form (**dissolved inorganic carbon** or DIC). DIC is present in several forms, of which dissolved CO_2 itself is only about 1%. Dissolved CO_2 reacts with water molecules (H_2O) to form hydrogen carbonate (HCO_3^-, also called bicarbonate), which comprises 91% of the DIC in the ocean. This reaction enables the ocean to store carbon from the atmosphere, but the ocean cannot take up carbon in this way indefinitely. A 100 p.p.m. increase in atmospheric CO_2 from today's levels will cause an increase in DIC, but this will be 40% less than the DIC increase that occurred when CO_2 rose 100 p.p.m. from pre-industrial levels to its present value of 380 p.p.m.. The oceans are becoming saturated with carbon.

The primary producers of the ocean are **phytoplankton** [mostly single-celled algae (protoctists) and bacteria] with an estimated GPP of 103 PgC yr^{-1}. This is disproportionately concentrated in coastal areas and parts of the ocean where nutrients are brought to the surface by upwelling currents. As in terrestrial ecosystems, about half of GPP is respired by autotrophs themselves. Grazing on phytoplankton by **zooplankton** consumes a greater fraction of NPP than herbivores on land do, but ultimately detritus from phytoplankton, zooplankton and larger marine animals sinks to depths of 100 m or more, carrying with it an estimated 11 PgC yr^{-1}, which is about 10% of GPP. At these depths, bacteria consume most of the detritus, respiring CO_2 and adding to the reservoir of DIC in the ocean. DIC is eventually returned to the surface by upwelling, usually at a distance from its place of origin. These mechanisms constitute a **biological pump** that raises the concentration of DIC in the deep ocean. It has been estimated that the biological pump lowers the atmospheric CO_2 concentration by about 200 p.p.m. compared with what it would otherwise be (Maier-Reimer et al., 1996).

1.4.3 How does biodiversity loss affect ecosystem functioning?

The last two sections have reviewed two important services that ecosystems provide. A question we have not addressed yet is, can ecosystems continue to function and to provide these services with reduced levels of biodiversity? To put it another way, how sustainable are ecosystem functions when species are lost? Clearly, if whole ecosystems are lost, then so are most if not all of their services.

- Which ecosystem services would you expect to be lost or reduced if a forest was felled and replaced by arable farming?

● Soil erosion would probably increase and carbon storage (in wood and soil) decrease. Depending on the geographical region and the extent of the deforestation, rainfall may be reduced. The quality of water from the catchment would almost certainly drop.

The consequences of losing biodiversity from otherwise intact ecosystems are less easy to predict. Clearly, this will depend on:

● which species are lost,

● what role those species played, and

● whether other species can take their place.

The answers to these questions will depend, at least in part, on local circumstances, but the ecological principles behind ecosystem function give us a guide to the likely consequences of biodiversity loss and explain some of the effects that have been observed. To understand ecosystem function, we first need to consider how ecosystems are structured. Refer back to Chapter 5 of Book 1, and Figure 1.11 in this chapter, and answer the following questions.

● How are ecosystems structured, and what roles do organisms in different parts of the structure play in the transfer of carbon and other materials?

● Ecosystems contain different trophic levels. Carbon and other materials are transferred between different levels when organisms in one level feed on organisms, their faeces or their remains in another.

The trophic levels, which we met earlier, are primary producers (plants), primary consumers (herbivores), secondary consumers (carnivores), detritivores and decomposers. There is often an additional tier in this structure containing **top carnivores**. Feeding relationships among organisms in an ecosystem create a **food web** that links trophic levels together, sometimes in complex ways. An example of a food web for the organisms in Wytham Wood near Oxford is shown in Figure 1.13.

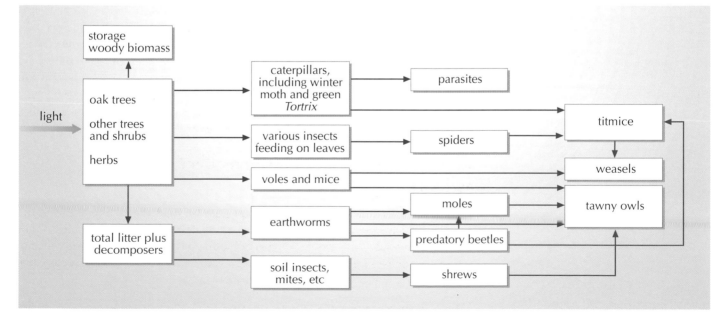

Figure 1.13 A simplified food web for Wytham Wood, near Oxford.

● Identify the main primary producers in the Wytham Wood ecosystem (Figure 1.13), and two species or groups in each of these trophic levels: detritivores, primary consumers, secondary consumers, top carnivores.

● The primary producers are oak trees, other trees, shrubs and herbs. Detritivores are earthworms, soil insects and mites; primary consumers are caterpillars and other insects and rodents (voles and mice); secondary consumers are spiders, parasites of caterpillars, predatory beetles, shrews, moles and titmice; top carnivores are weasels and tawny owls.

Most consumers feed upon more than one species of prey and the prey may be in the same or a lower trophic level. All higher trophic levels make inputs that are used by detritivores (note that these are not shown in Figure 1.13).

There are two fundamental ways in which the total biomass of organisms in one trophic level may be controlled by those in another level. They are are top-down control, in which organisms in the level above control production, and bottom-up control, in which control comes from the trophic level beneath.

Within a trophic level, abundance can also be controlled by competition between species. More complicated situations can also arise, with control of primary production by the nutrient supply and control of consumers by predation both occurring in the same ecosystem. Figure 1.14 illustrates some of the various possibilities in diagrammatic form.

● Describe which kind of control occurs in the ecosystem illustrated in Figure 1.14a.

● There is complete top-down control, in which each trophic level controls abundance in the level beneath.

Pure top-down control, with the consequences of the abundance in the carnivore trophic level cascading down to the abundance of plants at the bottom may occur in some freshwater aquatic ecosystems (Figure 1.15). Note that if top carnivores such as piscivorous (fish-eating) fish depress the numbers of their prey (planktivorous

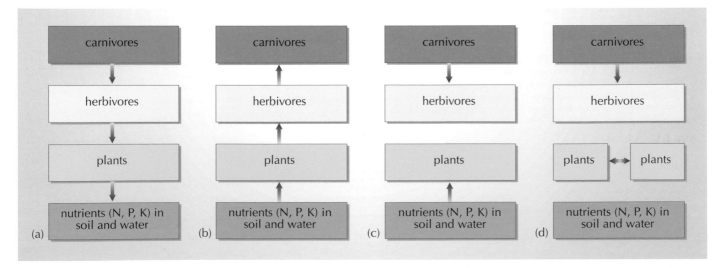

Figure 1.14 A range of possibilities for the control of the abundance of organisms in one trophic level by their resources (food or plant nutrients), by interactions within the trophic level, or by the next trophic level up. Arrows point from the controlling organisms or nutrient source to the controlled organisms or nutrient source.

fish in Figure 1.15), then the consequence will be that the food of those prey (large herbivores in Figure 1.15) will increase.

- If piscivorous fish were removed from the Wisconsin lake shown in Figure 1.15, what would you expect to happen to the abundance of phytoplankton?

- Phytoplankton abundance should increase. Removing piscivores would allow planktivorous fish to increase, this would depress the abundance of large herbivores, and that would allow large and small phytoplankton to increase in abundance.

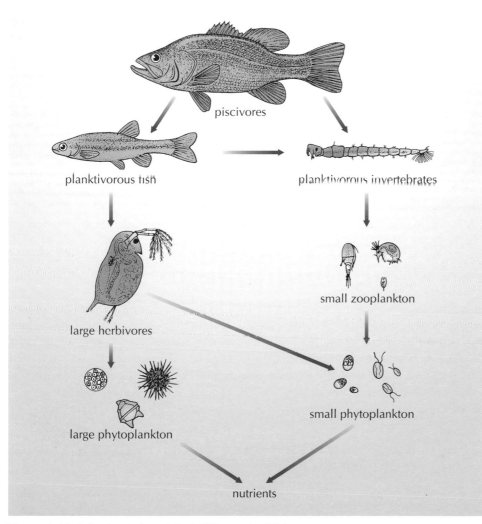

Figure 1.15 A food web for a lake in Wisconsin, USA.

- Describe which kind of control occurs in the ecosystem illustrated in Figure 1.14b.

- There is complete bottom-up control, in which each trophic level controls abundance in the level above.

No clear example of this situation is known, though it might be expected to occur where the supply of nutrients severely limits plant production (NPP). Herbivore numbers would need to be limited by food availability, rather than by predator numbers, for the bottom-up model to apply throughout the ecosystem. Bottom-up control is more likely to apply between just two trophic levels.

- Describe which kind of control occurs in the ecosystem illustrated in Figure 1.14c.

- There is top-down control of herbivores and bottom-up control of primary production in plants by their nutrient supply.

This is probably the most usual situation, particularly in terrestrial habitats. Herbivore numbers are controlled by predation and parasitism and are consequently held at a level that is too low to totally control the abundance of their food supply (plants). In the absence of control from above, primary production is determined by the rate of supply of nutrients or other resource (bottom-up). Ecosystems with more nutrient-rich soils, for example estuarine marshes that receive nutrient inputs in the form of silt, can have very high primary productivity. If carnivores are removed from systems like this, herbivore populations can explode and reach levels high enough to greatly reduce plant production. Over-exploitation of the plants by herbivores leads to soil erosion and destabilizes the ecosystem, because once plants become in short supply herbivore numbers will crash.

- Describe which kind of control occurs in the ecosystem illustrated in Figure 1.14d.

- Again there is top-down control of herbivores, but in this ecosystem plant productivity is controlled within the primary-producer trophic level.

Many experiments have been carried out with grassland plant communities to determine whether the number of species in the plant community affects its primary productivity. These studies have shown some significant positive effects of increasing the number of species, particularly in buffering (reducing) variation in plant productivity from year to year caused by variations in the weather. However, control of NPP by nutrient supply (e.g. Figure 1.14c) tends to be a stronger effect and also has an indirect effect on the number of plant species in the grassland community. Higher levels of nutrients increase productivity, but also decrease numbers of plant species because few plant species can compete successfully with fast-growing dominants when these have plenty of nutrients. Therefore, in nutrient-poor ecosystems the number of plant species may influence NPP, but this effect is probably absent from more productive ecosystems, if only because there are fewer plant species present.

1.5 How do we value species?

The existence of a species may be valuable to us in two distinct ways, direct and indirect. Many species are used directly to provide a material, such as wood, or food, such as fish. As you have seen, species may also be indirectly useful because they enable an ecosystem to function, and the ecosystem provides goods or services. The earthworms and honeybees in an orchard are indirectly useful in this way, although we have to understand something about the ecosystem to realize this.

1.5.1 Biodiversity in the marketplace

What is a species worth? This sounds like an impossible, perhaps even a nonsensical question until you realize just how much trade there is in natural products.

Activity 1.1

Write down ten items that appear on your regular shopping list, and then make a list of the species that supply these products and their ingredients. Use lists of ingredients on any packaging to help you. Before you start, make a guess at how many species you think you might reasonably have on the list when it is complete.

Comment

Our list (of 20 products) is in Table 1.2. It contains 30 different species. How near was your guess?

Now use your own list, or the one in Table 1.2, to work out the number of species that occur in only one product, in two products, or in more than two products. Use the axes provided in Figure 1.16 to draw a frequency distribution from these data, with the number of products (1, 2, 3, etc.) per species on the horizontal axis and the number of species that occur in one, two or three products on the vertical axis.

(a) What is the shape of this distribution, and what does it tell you about the contribution of species biodiversity to our diet?

(b) Which kinds of foods contain the most numbers of species and which the least?

Comment

Table 1.3 shows the results obtained from Table 1.2.

(a) Figure 1.17 shows the frequency distribution of the data in Table 1.3: it has a shape like an 'L'. This means that a lot of species occur in just one food product, while a few (e.g. wheat, milk and oil) occur in a great many. Soya bean flour is a widespread ingredient that happens not to be represented in our list in Table 1.2.

(b) We can conclude that the more processing that is involved in the production of a food item, the more species it contains.

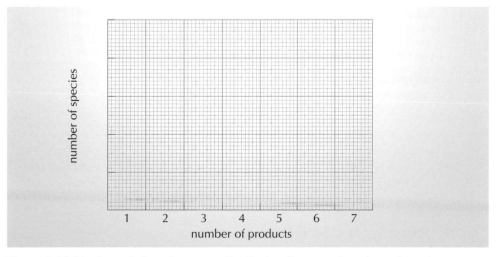

Figure 1.16 Blank graph for a frequency distribution diagram of numbers of species and products.

Table 1.2 A shopping list and the species that supply the products and their main ingredients. Some minor ingredients have been omitted.

Item	Species
Apples	*Malus domestica*
Baked beans	navy beans (*Phaseolus vulgaris*), tomato sauce ingredients (see below)
Bread	wheat (*Triticum aestivum*), yeast (*Saccharomyces cerevisiae*)
Cheese	milk
Cheese and onion crisps	potato (*Solanum tuberosum*), onion (*Allium* sp.), monosodium glutamate (MSG, produced from fermented sugar beet, *Beta vulgaris*), cheese flavour (milk product).
Eggs	from chickens (*Gallus domesticus*)
Fish fingers	cod (*Gadus morhua*), or one or more other whitefish species; wheat flour (*Triticum aestivum*); colour: annatto (from the tree *Bixa orellana*)
Frozen pizza	bread and cheese ingredients plus marjoram (*Origanum vulgare*)
Lettuce	*Lactuca sativa*
Margarine	sunflower oil (*Helianthus annuus*), colour: annatto (*B. orellana*)
Milk	from cows (*Bos domesticus*)
Minted Peas	peas (*Pisum sativum*), mint (*Mentha* sp.), sugar (probably from sugar beet *Beta vulgaris*)
Mushroom soup	mushrooms (*Boletus edulis* and other spp.), rapeseed oil (*Brassica napus*), wheat flour, maize starch (*Zea mays*), cream, monosodium glutamate (MSG), sherry (grapes *Vitis vinifera* fermented with yeast), pepper (*Piper* sp.)
Pork sausages	*Sus*, garlic (*Allium* sp.), bread ingredients
Sardines	*Sardinella* sp., sunflower oil (*Helianthus annuus*)
Strawberry yoghurt	milk, sugar (*B. vulgaris*), strawberry fruit (*Fragaria* sp.)
Tea bags	tea (leaves of *Camellia sinensis*), bag (fibre from the leaves of *Musa* sp.)
Toilet paper	wood pulp, probably from Norway spruce (*Picea abies*)
Tomato ketchup	tomato (*Lycopersicon esculentum*), yeast (and grain fermented to produce vinegar); sugar (probably from sugar beet *B. vulgaris*)
Vanilla ice cream	milk/cream (or non-dairy fat which could be of vegetable or animal origin), plus vanilla essence (probably an artificial mimic of the real flavour produced by the seed pods of the orchid *Vanilla* sp.), sugar (probably from sugar beet *B. vulgaris*)

Table 1.3 Frequency of occurrence of species contained in the products listed in Table 1.2.

Species or genus	Products	Total
Bos domesticus	milk, mushroom soup, cheese, yoghurt, ice cream, cheese and onion crisps, cheese in pizza	7
Beta vulgaris	ketchup, ice cream, MSG in soup and crisps, yoghurt, peas	6
Triticum aestivum	bread, fish fingers, mushroom soup, pork sausages, pizza	5

Saccharomyces cerevisiae	Yeast in bread, pizza, sherry in mushroom soup, vinegar in ketchup	4
Bixa orellana	colour in margarine, fish fingers	2
Helianthus annuus	margarine, sardines	2
Lycopersicon esculentum	ketchup, baked beans	2
Allium sp. (garlic)	pork sausages	1
Allium sp. (onion)	crisps	1
Boletus edulis	mushroom soup	1
Brassica napus	rapeseed oil in mushroom soup	1
Camellia sinensis	tea	1
Fragaria sp.	strawberry yoghurt	1
Gadus morhua	fish fingers	1
Gallus domesticus	eggs	1
Lactuca sativa	lettuce	1
Malus domestica	apples	1
Mentha sp.	minted peas	1
Musa sp.	tea bags	1
Origanum vulgare	pizza	1
Phaseolus vulgaris	baked beans	1
Picea abies	toilet paper	1
Piper sp.	pepper in mushroom soup	1
Pisum sativum	peas	1
Sardinella sp.	sardines	1
Solanum tuberosum	crisps	1
Sus sp.	pork sausages	1
Vanilla sp.	ice cream	1
Vitis vinifera	sherry in mushroom soup	1
Zea mays	maize starch in mushroom soup	1

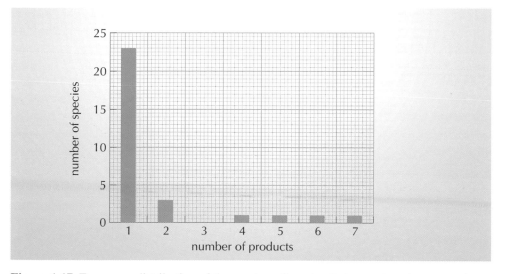

Figure 1.17 Frequency distribution of the number of species that occur in only one product, two products, etc., drawn from the data in Table 1.3.

Just a few species supply the staple foods of the human diet, but if you buy any processed foods or cook with herbs, spices and sauces at home, then you are also using the products of dozens more species.

Food staples vary with diet from one part of the world to another, but there is a striking similarity among the different staple foods: most are grasses. Wheat, rice, corn (maize), millet and sorghum all belong to the grass family. The grazing animals that are farmed for meat are also fed largely on grasses, and poultry are fed on grain. Sugar cane, a major source of sugar, is also a grass. To be sure, potato is an exception, but this is in the same plant family as tomato and chilli peppers, which are two other important food ingredients. Beans are an important source of vegetable protein and oil, and occur in another economically important plant family (the Fabaceae) that also contains peas, chick pea, lentils and plants such as clover and alfalfa that are important in the nutrition of grazing animals and in maintaining soil fertility. Plants in the bean family have the rare ability to turn atmospheric nitrogen gas into a chemical form that can be taken up and used by plants and other organisms. This **nitrogen fixation** is actually carried out by bacteria that inhabit nodules on the roots of most Fabaceae.

- If the staples of the human diet draw upon only a small fraction of all plant species, does this mean that most plant biodiversity is not valuable to human beings?

- There are at least four reasons why the answer to this question is an emphatic 'no'. First, a large number of non-staple food species are highly valued in their own right; second, the biodiversity represented by genetic variation *within* populations of the staple crops and their wild relatives is important for sustaining and improving yields of food crops; third, plants have other economic uses as sources of fuel, fibre, wood and pharmaceuticals; fourth, plants are key components of ecosystems and these have their own economic value.

One of the most obvious ways of stating the value of something is to give it an economic value – a price. Spices, particularly from the tropics, have long been one of the most highly priced derivatives of global biodiversity. In the 16th century one of the rarest and costliest spices was nutmeg, the seed of a large tree *Myristica fragrans*, which is native to a handful of small islands in the Indonesian Moluccas. Giles Milton, author of a fascinating account of the English and other European expeditions mounted to reach the 'Spiceries' where nutmeg grew, writes that such was the value of nutmeg in late 16th century London that 'A small sackful was enough to set a man up for life, buying him a gabled dwelling in Holborn and a servant to attend to his needs.' Indeed, the European exploration of Asia was initially motivated by the high price that spices fetched on home markets. Even the discovery of the Americas was an accidental by-product of the search for a western route to the Indies and their botanical and other treasures.

From the perspective of the evolution of biodiversity, it is worth considering *why* plants are such a rich source of useful chemical compounds with biological activity. Take chillies for example. The compound that makes chillies taste hot is called **capsaicin**. Experiments performed with wild chillies have shown that this substance is not distasteful to birds, but that rodents avoid chilli seeds and also palatable seeds that have been dosed with capsaicin. Birds are particularly attracted to the red fruit, eat the chilli and disperse its seeds when these are deposited in their faeces. Capsaicin is a biologically selective, defensive compound that prevents chilli seeds being eaten by rodents, which are major predators of seeds.

Closer to home, mustard is another example of a spice that we find stimulatory when added to our food, but which deters herbivores from eating plants that manufacture it. The compounds in question belong to a group known as **glucosinolates**, which are found in most plants belonging to the cabbage family. The smell of glucosinolates may be familiar to you — it is the smell of boiling cabbage. One of the defensive functions of glucosinolates in oilseed rape, which belongs to the cabbage family, was discovered when plant breeders produced a variety with lower than normal levels of the compound. Fields of low-glucosinolate oilseed rape were attacked by a fungal pathogen, which destroyed the crop. Glucosinolates in cabbages protect against both insect and fungal natural enemies. Capsaicin, glucosinolates and hundreds of thousands of other chemical compounds produced by plants appear to be the products of millions of years of evolution in which plants have evolved deterrents and toxins against their natural enemies.

- Why is there such variety in the chemical defences evolved by plants? Once defences that work have evolved, shouldn't their evolution just stop?

- If it *were* possible to evolve permanent protection against insect herbivores or fungi, then the evolution of novel chemical compounds might indeed cease. However, it seems that permanent protection cannot be achieved.

The reason why chemical defences appear to have diversified rather than come to a halt during evolutionary history is that every novel defence by a plant gives an advantage to any natural enemy able to evolve a means of overcoming that defence. Natural enemies with this advantage spread, and thus the enemy population evolves along with the plant population. This process is called **coevolution** and has been compared to an arms-race. Glucosinolates do help protect cabbages, but if you have ever tried to grow them in your garden you will know that glucosinolates do not seem to deter the caterpillars of cabbage white butterflies. The evolutionary arms-race between plants and herbivores is a ceaseless one. Genetic variation is the raw material of evolution, and within populations it plays an important role in the evolution of defence. This is one of the functions served by genetic variation in crop plants and their wild relatives. These processes of coevolution are part and parcel of biological diversity. Hence, although the value of some features of biodiversity may not always be easily visible (indeed, they do on many occasions cost us, such as with a ruined crop of cabbages), it seems that all these features matter to us profoundly.

1.5.2 The value of genetic variation in domesticated species

Our crop plants and farm animals are descended from wild ancestors that were mostly domesticated in the Near East during the Neolithic Period (around 7000 BC). Their origin illustrates how humans have used the genetic resources of wild populations and why, where wild populations of ancestors still exist, these are potentially invaluable sources for the further genetic improvement of our crops.

During domestication, neolithic farmers, consciously or not, selected individuals from wild populations that, in the case of animals, were more docile, and, in the case of plants, did not shed their grain before it could be harvested, as wild plants invariably do. Heritable variation in these characteristics must have existed in wild populations for these early attempts at domestication to succeed. In effect, what early farmers did was to mimic the evolutionary process of natural selection by selectively propagating genotypes that showed the characteristics that they preferred.

Where natural selection differs from artificial selection is that nature, rather than the breeder, provides the selective force that causes some genotypes to propagate in preference to others. Natural selection is blind to the end result, whereas a breeder performing artificial selection has a particular end in view. In either case, the genotypes that spread are those that, for whatever reason, are most successful in contributing offspring to future generations. For example, in a habitat where wild chillies grow, a rodent that has a genotype that allows it to tolerate capsaicin will be well-provided with seeds that other rodents cannot eat. One can easily imagine how this extra supply of food could cause rodents with the capsaicin-tolerating genotype to increase, even to the point of replacing the capsaicin-intolerant genotype.

Because genetic variation is the raw material on which selection, be it artificial or natural, operates we need to know where to find it. The question is not just where on Earth to find, say, wheat genes (although that is important), but whether genetic variation in wheat is to be found mainly within polymorphic populations or whether it is mainly distributed between populations.

●   Figure 1.18 shows two scenarios for the distribution of variation in populations. Identify the two types of variation illustrated.

●   Figure 1.18a shows a scenario in which each population is a different colour, so variation in the species as a whole resides between populations. In Figure 1.18b, each population contains every colour, so there is little variation between populations and most of the variation is found within populations.

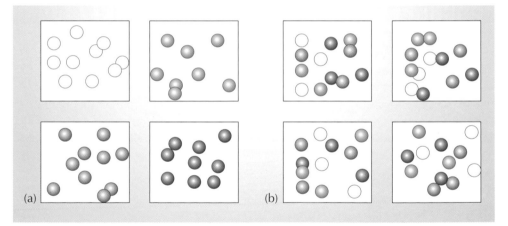

Figure 1.18 Two scenarios for the distribution of variation in populations.

The reason why the distribution of genetic variation is important is that if most of it can be found as polymorphism *within* populations, then genetic biodiversity can be maintained by protecting relatively few populations. If, on the other hand, most populations are different from one another then all must be preserved in order to protect the genetic biodiversity of a species.

It turns out that in most crop species there is a lot of genetic variation *between* populations. By contrast, genetic variation in the human population is much higher within populations than between them. What we think of as 'racial' differences between human populations are merely superficial, and at the genetic level human populations are much more like Figure 1.18b than Figure 1.18a.

In general, the distribution of genetic variation within and between populations is determined largely by patterns of mating. Mating between genetically dissimilar individuals produces offspring with genotypes that combine genes from both parents and which may be entirely new. This source of genetic variation is absent when similar individuals mate, the ultimate example of this being in hermaphrodites when male and female parents may be one and the same individual. The wild progenitors of most crop plants, such as wheat, are hermaphrodites that are largely self-pollinating. This pattern of inbreeding is continued, or even intensified, when species are domesticated because the best way to breed for a desired character, such as large grain size, is to self-pollinate, or to confine crosses to a handful of individuals in which the trait is displayed to an extreme.

Continued inbreeding produces genetic uniformity within populations and tends to lead to genetic divergence between populations. On the other hand, outcrossing maintains genetic variation and reduces the tendency for populations to diverge genetically. Humans are outbreeding, with marriage between close family members forbidden in nearly all cultures, which is why human populations maintain genetic diversity.

The geographical spread of domesticated animals and plants led to the formation of many divergent local populations wherever farmers selected the genotypes that grew best in their particular situation, or where they simply chose to breed from animals that they liked the look of. This is how, although domestication originally occurred in Asia, Britain became a centre of genetic biodiversity for sheep, with scores of local breeds recognized and maintained.

The evolution of **landraces**, as the locally selected varieties of crop plants are called, and their contribution to the breeding of modern crops is succinctly described by Frankel:

> When wheat reached China 3000 years after its domestication in the Near East, many types evolved that are peculiar to that region. Some, very likely evolved under irrigation, have ears with unusually large numbers of spikelets, and spikelets with unusually large numbers of grains. Wheat was carried across the Sea of Japan; and one may guess that it was this same character combination which, possibly centuries later, reappeared in a modern Japanese wheat, Norin 10, to find its way into Vogel's record-yielding hybrids and ultimately into the high-yielding Mexican varieties which helped to introduce the 'green revolution' in countries of Asia and Latin America.
>
> (Frankel, 1995)

Landraces are the repositories of highly valuable genetic resources. The sad irony is that the globalized process of modern plant breeding described by Frankel threatens the continued existence of the very landraces that are its raw material. Once they are widely available, farmers prefer high-yielding varieties and stop growing local landraces. High yields also require high inputs of fertilizers, herbicides and pesticides, which can damage the habitats adjacent to fields where, in the regions of domestication, wild relatives may grow next to crops and exchange genes with them by occasional cross-pollination (Ellstrand et al., 1999). Increasingly, the genetic biodiversity of landraces has come to reside in cold storage in seed banks rather than in evolving populations in the field.

We may ask whether landraces and wild crop populations are needed any more, or perhaps consider their loss an unfortunate but justifiable price to pay for the high yields of modern varieties. There is a good reason why to take this view would be short-sighted. That reason is disease. Every population of every living organism is assailed by disease-causing microbes (pathogens), such as bacteria, viruses and fungi. Even bacteria and fungi are infected by viruses. Crops grown in large acreages of a single kind (**monocultures**) are particularly susceptible and are attacked by specific pathogens. For example, separate forms of black stem rust (a fungus) belonging to the species *Puccinia graminis*, attack different cereal crops. One occurs mostly on wheat, another mainly on rye, barley and couch grass, and another on oats and cocksfoot grass. Genetic differences between grass species confer resistance to some genotypes of *P. graminis* but not others, but there is even more subtle genetic variation in disease resistance *within* crop species.

As a rule, the variation in disease resistance within crop species is matched by corresponding genetic variation for successful infection, or **virulence**, in the pathogen species that attack them. The situation is rather as if every variety of a crop has its own specific diseases.

○ What would you expect to happen to a crop containing plants that were genetically identical with each other?

● They would all be susceptible to the same strain of disease. With so many identical hosts available, this disease strain would spread rapidly, with catastophic results for the crop.

Genetically diverse crop populations that contain plants with different genotypes are better protected against pathogens because the plants susceptible to any particular pathogen strain are hidden amongst plants that are resistant. Genetic diversity in crops appears to be vital if yields are to be sustainable in environments where both the climate and the risk of disease vary.

Before the genetic relationships between crops and their diseases were fully understood, crop breeders producing genetically uniform new varieties found themselves on a treadmill, constantly having to come up with new varieties that were resistant to the then-most-prevalent pathogen genotype. In the 1930s, the Marquis variety of wheat suffered severe epidemics of black stem rust in North America. The variety Ceres was produced by crossing Marquis with a variety named Kota that was resistant, but this succumbed to a new rust genotype in 1935. The variety Thatcher was successful until 1940, but proved susceptible to brown rust, *Puccinia recondita*. Potato breeders found themselves on a similar treadmill caused by the potato blight organism *Phytophthora infestans*; this does occur in populations of wild potatoes, but does not cause epidemics because the genetic diversities of plant and pathogen apparently prevent this.

Modern plant breeding has slowed down the treadmill by incorporating genetic diversity into crops in various ways. Varieties have been produced that contain resistance genes against several pathogen genotypes, and genes that confer a degree of disease tolerance have been used. Such plants become infected, but show less severe symptoms. These genes have often come from wild populations.

Attempts have been made to quantify the economic value of some wild populations that are the source of genes useful in plant breeding. For example, one of the ancestors of domesticated corn is a wild grass called teosinte, *Euchlaena mexicana*, which is found in the Mexican state of Jalisco. A value of US$230–330 million has been placed on the genes for virus resistance that are found in teosinte in Jalisco. This would all have been lost if the land had been converted to intensive agriculture.

1.5.3 Non-food uses of biodiversity

Biodiversity is an evolutionary heritage, and this has given us much more than just food. Some other marketable functions of biodiversity are:

- Fibre-producing plants and animals that provide cotton, linen (from flax), paper pulp and wool.

- Fuel from renewable sources such as coppiced willow.

- Latex from rubber trees, which is preferred to synthetic rubber for many uses, such as the manufacture of condoms.

- Ornamental species including tens of thousands of plant species grown for their flowers or foliage, and tropical fish kept as pets.

- Eco-tourism, which is of growing importance in the tourist trade.

- Construction materials, particularly wood and bamboo.

- Biological monitors of air pollution (e.g. lichens) and water quality (e.g. stream invertebrates).

- Biological control agents that can be used against pests. For example, the bacterium *Bacillus thuringiensis* is used against caterpillars and parasitoid wasps are used against aphids and scale insects.

- Decontamination by microbes that are able to degrade pollutants such as *Fusarium* species that degrade cyanide in contaminated soil or marine bacteria that consume oil spilled by tankers.

- Pharmaceuticals, particularly from plants, and some of which are now synthesized to mimic the natural product. Classic examples are salicylic acid (aspirin) from willows and the anti-malarial drug quinine from the cinchona tree. Penicillin and other antibiotics are found in fungi.

Figures for its monetary value are useful reminders that biodiversity represents 'natural capital', but it would be dangerous to forget that, unlike other forms of capital, once it is extinct biodiversity cannot be brought (or bought) back. Actual market valuations depend upon someone's willingness to pay a particular price, but the monetary value ascribed to biodiversity is not determined in an auction. Instead, such values are calculated by adding up the financial losses that would hypothetically result if the biodiversity resource disappeared. Such an exercise involves large uncertainties, which might easily undervalue a resource. However, there is also a more fundamental problem. Relying entirely on market value to protect a resource means you have to accept that there *is* a price at which you would be prepared to see a species go extinct. The market has no interest in anything except the financial return on capital. If the current rate of return on money invested in biodiversity is less than the current rate of return on property speculation, the market will opt for building skyscrapers on nature reserves. Though it is true that as space for biodiversity diminishes its market value will probably increase through scarcity, you cannot order-up extinct species to satisfy a new demand.

1.6 Summary of Chapter 1

1.1 Biodiversity, broadly defined, is all hereditarily based variation from genes, through species to ecosystems. A narrower definition that equates biodiversity with the number of species in an area is often used.

1.2　The collection of species in a particular habitat is described as a community, and a community plus its non-living physical environment comprises an ecosystem. The living and non-living components of ecosystems are linked by transfers of carbon and other chemical elements between them.

1.3　There are three kinds of reason why biodiversity matters to people: its aesthetic value, its utility and moral reasons. In addition to the direct value of species that provide goods, such as food and timber, biodiversity plays a part in the services that ecosystems provide. Examples of ecosystem services are as storage reservoirs in the carbon cycle and in water processing.

1.4　According to the biological species concept, a species is defined as a distinct biological entity that does not interbreed with other species.

1.5　Species extinction is a normal evolutionary process, but the high proportion of species that are threatened with extinction today suggests that human actions are leading to a mass extinction of crisis proportions. The consequences of these extinctions for ecosystem function will depend on which species are affected and what role they play. In addition to the use-value of crops and species harvested from the wild, biodiversity at the genetic level of organization has value because crops lacking genetic diversity are particularly susceptible to disease.

Learning Outcomes for Chapter 1

When you have completed this chapter you should be able to:

1.1　Define and use, or recognize definitions and applications of, each of the terms printed in **bold** in the text. (Question 1.1)

1.2　Discuss, illustrate by examples, and distinguish between aesthetic, moral and usefulness arguments for the conservation of biodiversity. (Question 1.2)

1.3　Discuss the uncertainties involved in estimating current extinction rates for species. (Question 1.3)

1.4　Discuss, by reference to named examples, the relationship between biodiversity and sustainability. (Question 1.4)

Questions for Chapter 1

Answer the following questions in no more than 100 words each.

Question 1.1

In a single paragraph define the terms biodiversity, ecosystem and carbon cycle, and show how they relate to each other.

Question 1.2

By reference to a named example, describe how the aesthetic and usefulness arguments for the conservation of biodiversity are related to each other.

Question 1.3

What are the uncertainties involved in estimating current extinction rates for species?

Question 1.4

How can the sustainability of crop yield depend on some aspects of biodiversity?

References

Bailey, L. H. (1922) *The Apple Tree*. New York: The Macmillan Company.

Darwin, C. (1996/1859) *The Origin of Species*, 6th edn. Oxford: Oxford University Press.

Ellstrand, N. C., Prentice, H. C. and Hancock, J. F. (1999) Gene flow and introgression from domesticated plants into their wild relatives. *Annual Review of Ecology and Systematics*, **30**, pp. 539–563.

Frankel, O. H. (1995) The genetic diversity of cultivated plants. In Frankel, O. H., Brown, A. H. D. and Burdon, J. J. (eds) *The Conservation of Plant Biodiversity*. Chapter 3, pp. 39–78. Cambridge: Cambridge University Press.

Houghton, J. T., Ding, Y., Griggs, D. J., Noguer, M., van der Linden, P. J., Dai, X., Maskell, K. and Johnson, C. A. (eds) (2001) *Climate Change 2001: The Scientific Basis*. Cambridge: Cambridge University Press.

Juniper, B. (2000) Prehistoric pippins. *Oxford Today*, **13**, pp. 28–30.

Lomborg, B. (2001) *The Skeptical Environmentalist*. Cambridge: Cambridge University Press.

Maier-Reimer, E., Mikolajewicz, U. and Winguth, A. (1996) Future ocean uptake of CO_2 – interaction between ocean circulation and biology. *Climate Dynamics*, **12**, pp. 711–721.

Milton, G. (1999) *Nathaniel's Nutmeg*. London: Hodder & Stoughton.

Myers, N., Mittermeier, R. A., Mittermeier, C. G., da Fonseca, G. A. B. and Kent, J. (2000) Biodiversity hotspots for conservation priorities. *Nature*, **403**, pp. 853–858.

Schumacher, E. F. (1973) *Small is Beautiful*. New York: Harper and Row.

Shapiro, J. (2001) *Mao's War against Nature*. Cambridge: Cambridge University Press.

Wilson, E. O. (1994) *Naturalist*. London: Little Brown.

Wilson, E. O. (1997) Introduction. In Reaka-Kudla, M. L., Wilson, D. E. and Wilson, E. O. (eds) *Biodiversity II: Understanding and Protecting our Biological Resources*. Washington, D. C.: Joseph Henry Press.

Chapter 2 A global perspective on people and ecosystems

Prepared for the course team by Jonathan Silvertown

2.1 Introduction to *World Resources: The Fraying Web of Life*

This is the first of two chapters based on the book *World Resources: The Fraying Web of Life* (*WR*). We have chosen to include *WR* as a part of U316 because it takes an authoritative and multi-disciplinary approach to biodiversity and ecosystems. The book is global in its perspective and it emphasizes practical arguments in favour of protecting biodiversity and ecosystems. A clear exposition of the scope of environmental problems is given, as well as examples of solutions and good environmental practice. The arguments in *WR* are based on quantitative assessments of ecosystems, and it is possible to trace the evidence used back to its source. This is not the same as saying that every number is accurate. Indeed, a recurring theme in *WR* is that more work needs to be done on evaluating human impacts upon ecosystems.

You should read *WR* section by section, as guided by the study notes in this chapter and the next. Each study note is flagged with a marginal icon.

The questions related to *WR* are to be found at the end of each section, rather than at the end of each chapter as in the rest of U316. This enables you to use the questions to test your understanding of *WR* as you read through it. Answers to questions will be found at the back of this book.

> As elsewhere, web activities are signposted at appropriate points. Now would be a good time to do the activities associated with this chapter.

2.2 *WR* Chapter 1: Linking people and ecosystems

> Read *WR* pp. v–ix, which contain the Contents and Foreword. While reading the Foreword, make a list of a dozen keywords that you think sum up the stated aims of *WR*.

Question 2.1

Compare the keywords and phrases you chose while reading *WR* with the list in the answer to this question.

Question 2.2

What is meant by 'adopting an ecosystems approach', and how is this linked to sustainability?

2.2.1 Ecosystem goods and services

Continue reading the *WR* text to the bottom of p. 15. While reading this section make a list of a dozen keywords and phrases that describe goods and services provided by ecosystems.

Question 2.3

Compare the keywords and phrases you chose while reading *WR* with the list in the answer to this question.

The **goods-and-services approach** to ecosystems taken by *WR* is part of mainstream thought on the subject, but there are those in the field of ecological economics who challenge it. A debate on this question was launched after an article by Robert Costanza and others that appeared in 1997 put a value of US$33 trillion on the goods and services produced by all ecosystems globally – a sum considerably greater than the world's entire Gross National Product at that time. There followed a rash of articles in the world press about the value of nature. However, a number of criticisms emerged. For example, Mark Sagoff (1998) argued that methodological and philosophical problems abound when we try to value nature. He criticized the methods used to value goods and services as unsound because they differed from those used in the wider market place. The price of a ship is based on what it will fetch in a competitive market, while ecosystem goods and services have to be valued by looking at outputs or replication costs. He argued that Costanza had forgotten the insights of the 18th century economist Adam Smith, who distinguished between 'value in use' and 'value in exchange'. Water has incalculable 'value in use', and very little 'value in exchange', whereas the exact reverse applies to diamond.

In an essay entitled 'The Ecological Tyranny of the Bottom Line', John Bellamy Foster (2002) more generally attacked the idea that the environment is being turned into a set of commodities. He argued that economic production depends on nature, but that this relationship cannot be reduced to market economics. He too distinguished between market price and intrinsic value, arguing that it is common sense that the latter cannot be reduced to the former. His conclusion was that the current capitalist economic system is ecologically unsustainable, both intrinsically and irreformably.

None of these critics directly attacks *WR* itself, which uses the goods-and-services model qualitatively rather than quantitatively, but these arguments should encourage you to think critically about what you read in *WR*, regardless of whether you agree or disagree with it.

2.2.2 Human impacts on ecosystems

Read *WR* pp. 16–29, which, broadly, survey the impacts of human exploitation upon ecosystems that threaten their sustainability. While reading this section make a list of a dozen keywords and phrases that describe some of the kinds of impact that humans have on ecosystems.

Question 2.4

Compare the keywords and phrases that you chose while reading *WR* with the list in the answer to this question.

Question 2.5

Why can it be difficult to determine when an ecosystem has been exploited to the point of unsustainability?

2.2.3 The economics of ecosystem exploitation

Read *WR* pp. 30–41 and then answer the following questions.

Question 2.6

How can subsidies be environmentally damaging? Give two examples.

Question 2.7

Apart from subsidies, what three other types of 'policy failure' are discussed? Give one example of how each can damage ecosystems.

Question 2.8

Name at least three methods that are used by environmental economists to place a value on ecosystem goods and services. What are their limitations?

Question 2.9

Explain the term 'trade-off', using examples from ecotourism to illustrate your answer.

Question 2.10

How can patterns of ownership affect (a) the sustainability of ecosystem exploitation and (b) adaptation by rural peoples to environmental change?

Refer to the U316 website for activities relating to *WR* Chapter 1.

2.3 Summary of Chapter 2

2.1   Chapter 1 of *WR*, 'Linking people and ecosystems', argues that human well-being and the global economy are both underpinned by the goods and services provided by ecosystems.

2.2   Examples of goods include food and fibre crops, fish, timber and genetic resources for crop breeding. Examples of services provided by ecosystems include watershed protection and climate control, crop pollination, soil production and carbon sequestration.

2.3   Decisions about how to manage ecosystems involve trade-offs between the costs and benefits of any action.

2.4   Ecosystems may collapse if exploitation pushes them over a threshold of sustainability.

2.5   Amongst other threats, natural ecosystems can be degraded by overharvesting (e.g. overfishing), conversion to cropland or urban use, soil erosion and overexploitation of groundwater.

2.6 Invasion by non-native organisms also threatens biodiversity in many ecosystems.

2.7 The ownership of resources (or ecosystems) affects how they are exploited and whether exploitation is sustainable or not.

2.8 How ecosystems may be managed for sustainable production, in general, requires further research.

Learning Outcomes for Chapter 2

When you have completed Chapter 2 you should be able to:

2.1 Define, recognize and use correctly terms shown in **bold** in the text and/or listed in the Glossary.

2.2 Identify keywords and concepts used in *World Resources*. (Questions 2.1, 2.3 and 2.4).

2.3 Giving relevant examples, discuss the role of uncertainty, economic and social factors and the 'ecosystems approach' to sustainability. (Questions 2.2, 2.5–2.10).

References

Costanza, R., d'Arge, R., de Groot, R., Farber, S., Grasso, M., Hannon, B., Limburg, K., Naeem, S., O'Neill, R. V., Paruelo, J., Raskin, R. G., Sutton, P. and van den Belt, M. (1997) The value of the world's ecosystem services and natural capital. *Nature*, **387**, pp. 253–260. Reprinted in: *Ecological Economics*, 1998, **25**, pp. 3–15. This journal is available electronically through the OU Library (go to http://library.open.ac.uk/resources/ejournals/ejournals_e.html and click on Ecological Economics).

Foster, J. B. (2002) The ecological tyranny of the bottom line. in *Ecology against Capitalism*, New York: Monthly Review Press.

Sagoff, M. (1998) Can we put a price on nature's services? Available on the website of The Institute for Philosophy and Public Policy, http://www.puaf.umd.edu/IPPP/NATURE.HTM [Accessed 7 October 2002]

Chapter 3 Threats to ecosystems and biodiversity

Prepared for the course team by Irene Ridge

3.1 Introduction

From Chapters 1 and 2 you have a general understanding of ecosystem services and of biodiversity. In this chapter we want you to explore further the various threats to ecosystems using *World Resources* (*WR*) as your main source of information. Chapters 2 and 3 of *WR* are the most relevant but, rather than reading straight through these chapters, we suggest that you use them as a reference source to answer the questions and carry out the activities in the text here. You will need to read (or re-read) parts of these *WR* chapters when studying later books in the course.

In the following sections you will progress from a broad view of ecosystem change and threats to stability (Section 3.2), to focusing on particular threats (alien species, disturbance/habitat loss, pollution) and the effects that they have had on different ecosystems (Sections 3.3–3.6).

3.2 What threats?

On a geological scale of many thousands or millions of years there has been constant change in ecosystems, punctuated by mass extinction events when up to 95% of known species disappeared — and some part of the biosphere has always recovered. On a human or historical time-scale, however, even small changes in the way that ecosystems function are a threat because they affect vital services that support human society. This is the point of view that dominates *WR* and, as argued in *WR* Chapter 1, it is human population growth and consumption that are the main (although by no means the only) drivers of ecosystem change, including loss of biodiversity.

> Bearing in mind the human perspective taken by *WR*, read now the first part of Chapter 2 (pp. 43–52) to obtain an expert assessment of the condition of five major ecosystems and their capacity to provide a range of goods and services relevant to humans.

Question 3.1

According to **PAGE's ecosystem scorecard** (p. 47): (a) which ecosystem is in the worst overall condition?; (b) in which ecosystem is there evidence of a trade-off between the provision of different services?

Question 3.2

In one or two sentences (30–50 words) summarize the overall situation for the five ecosystems shown in the PAGE scorecard.

Question 3.3

Which of the goods and services listed in the PAGE scorecard appears to be in the worst state and which in the next worst state?

Question 3.4

List the main limitations or problems with the PAGE approach to ecosystem assessment.

The PAGE study is probably the most comprehensive attempt so far to assess the state of Earth's ecosystems but, as acknowledged in *WR*, it has weaknesses.

3.3 Biodiversity

The nature and significance of biodiversity were topics explored in Chapter 1 of this book, but here we want you to go further, using *WR* as the main source of information to answer four fundamental questions:

1   Is the global decline in biodiversity evenly spread?

The data in *WR* cover only five types of ecosystem and are admitted to be scanty, but they indicate that there is considerable variability in the state of biodiversity between ecosystems.

2   What are the main causes of biodiversity decline?

You need to sift through information in *WR* to find answers but the underlying, if not the immediate, cause of declining global biodiversity is widely considered to be human population growth and use of resources.

3   What is being or could be done to counter threats to biodiversity?

Case studies in *WR* Chapter 3 provide some answers.

4   Does declining biodiversity matter?

This is the thorniest question of all and was raised in Chapter 1. The eminent ecologist Lord Robert May has expressed the view 'I think it possible that we are clever enough to live in a hugely simplified world', i.e. high biodiversity is not necessary in order for ecosystems to continue supplying essential services (such as water purification). No one knows if Lord May is right but, supposing he were, would we *want* to live in such a simplified world with greatly reduced biodiversity?

With these questions as a framework, you should now tackle reading *WR* (the rest of Chapter 2 and Chapter 3) and the questions. These are divided into five sections: one for each of four different ecosystem types and a fifth that looks at interactions between types.

You can tackle the questions in various ways:

- Simply work through each set of questions: this involves reading parts of *WR* Chapters 2 and 3 relevant to five ecosystems and answering questions that test your understanding of *WR*;
- Look through (skim read) *WR* Chapters 2 and 3, and then work through the questions, re-reading material so that you can answer questions;

- Read carefully through *WR* Chapters 2 and 3, and then try to answer the questions associated with each section, using *WR* simply as a source of reference.

Instructions for questions assume that you are using the first approach. However, the remainder of *WR* Chapter 2 (pp. 53–145) is written more as a catalogue of facts than for easy reading, so you might find it easier to use it as a reference source. The case studies in *WR* Chapter 3, on the other hand, require reading through carefully and, although not all are relevant to the issue of biodiversity, they are relevant to later chapters of this book and to later books in the course.

Sections 3.3.1–3.3.4 each relate to a particular type of ecosystem (excluding agroecosystems).

3.3.1 Coastal ecosystems

Coastal ecosystems are defined very broadly in *WR* as 'regions (in) the intertidal and subtidal areas above the continental shelf (to a depth of 200 m) and adjacent land area up to 100 km inland from the coast'. Inevitably, very different ecosystems are included, ranging from coral reefs and shallow off-shore waters to mangroves, salt marshes and classic sandy or rocky shores. This diversity is acknowledged in *WR* (p. 69) but it does make generalizations particularly difficult. Only in a few areas where there are vast coastal marshes or large estuaries can the coastal influence be regarded as penetrating as far as 100 km inland.

Activity 3.1   Coastal ecosystems in the UK

As a way of 'tuning in' to coastal ecosystems, based on your own experience of them, list the main types of coastal ecosystem that occur around the UK and, for each type, state what you think are the main services it provides.

Answer

The main types of coastal ecosystem are:

- *Offshore waters*, which act as fishing grounds (providing food for humans), a habitat or feeding place for wildlife, areas for leisure activities (sailing and angling, for example), and dumping grounds for wastes, ranging from mildly radioactive discharges from nuclear power stations to sewage (usually purified).
- *Salt marshes*, which are important sites for wildlife, including many birds; they act as a protective barrier for inland areas; and may provide grazing for farm livestock; drained marshes are much used as agricultural land.
- *Estuaries*, which are commonly linked to salt marshes, are also important wildlife sites. In addition they may be used by fishermen and boating enthusiasts and help to purify river water containing pollutants from inland sites.
- *Sandy coasts*, which are a major site for tourism and leisure activities, often protect inland regions from the sea, and have their own suite of specialized species (especially the sand dunes).
- *Rocky coasts*, which are most often appreciated for their wildlife and beauty, and can be equated with a tourism/leisure function.

Now attempt Questions 3.5–3.8, using *WR* pp. 69–85 as a source of information and reading the case studies on pp. 163–180.

Question 3.5

What are the three main factors that have caused global loss of biodiversity in coastal ecosystems?

Question 3.6

What other factors have contributed to the global decline in coastal ecosystems (and may be major factors in some geographical areas)?

Question 3.7

From the case studies in *WR* Chapter 3, describe briefly three examples that illustrate how habitat destruction or damage has affected coastal marine biodiversity.

Question 3.8

What is the main difference between the case of South Florida on the one hand and Mankòtè and Bolinao on the other in the approach to governance taken in restoring coastal ecosystems and biodiversity?

3.3.2 Forest ecosystems

Ancient forests are the most complex of all terrestrial ecosystems, with high biodiversity and myriad interactions between organisms that take decades to establish. These interactions involve a wide variety of organisms — plants, fungi, insects, mammals, birds and many more — so that simply planting trees does not create a biologically diverse forest. Given also that many forest species have poor powers of dispersal, it may take hundreds of years to develop a species-rich forest. It follows that a major conservation priority is the protection or maintenance of existing ancient forests.

However, such concern for ancient forests does not imply that they cannot be used by humans. The great value of forests for human development is described in detail in *WR* Chapter 2 and the need for wise, sustainable use of forests is illustrated graphically in the forest case studies in Chapter 3.

Using *WR* pp. 87–102 and the case studies on pp. 181–192 as a source of information, attempt Questions 3.9–3.11.

Question 3.9

According to *WR*, what single factor is the greatest threat to forest ecosystems?

Question 3.10

Identify three other factors that have contributed significantly to the loss of forest biodiversity.

Question 3.11

In the Dhani forest (India), what were the proximate (immediate) causes of forest decline and loss of biodiversity?

3.3.3 Freshwater ecosystems

You will study problems related to water supply in Block 4, but here we are concerned with the overall value of, and threats to, freshwater ecosystems. Their direct value to human populations is inestimable and, indeed, there is evidence that the demise of some ancient civilizations (e.g. ancient Egypt) was caused by failing water supplies. Most (around 69%) of the water used by humans is for irrigation, i.e. food supplies, and there are often major conflicts between the human need for water and maintaining freshwater biodiversity. Understanding how freshwater ecosystems function and balancing their sustainable use with human needs is — or should be — a key aim.

> Using *WR* pp. 103–118 and the case studies on pp. 193–211 as a source of information, answer Questions 3.12–3.16.

Question 3.12

What are the three main factors that have caused global loss of biodiversity in freshwater ecosystems?

Question 3.13

What other factors have contributed to the global decline in freshwater ecosystems (and may be major factors in some geographical areas)?

Question 3.14

What are the perceived economic benefits from damming and diverting the Mekong River, and to which countries do the benefits accrue?

Question 3.15

(a) What are the known or probable adverse effects with respect to ecosystem services that result from damming or diversion of the Mekong River? Which countries would be most severely affected? (b) What kind of governance is involved in the project?

Question 3.16

What are the two main driving forces that led to the New York City watershed protection plan?

3.3.4 Grassland ecosystems

In their assessment of grassland ecosystems (*WR* Chapter 2), PAGE researchers admit to using a broad definition, which ranges from tundra to open, grassy woodlands. You should bear this in mind because, inevitably, it reduces the reliability of generalizations. Nevertheless, grasslands do occupy a large part of the land area, as stated in *WR*, and have been the prime sites for agriculture.

In the UK it is sheep grazing that maintains most of the apparently natural upland grasslands, as they would probably revert to forest — the true climax vegetation — if left ungrazed. In other parts of the world, grasslands are maintained by a variety of factors, some natural (e.g. natural fires and grazing and low rainfall or temperature, which prevent tree growth) and some caused by humans (e.g. stock grazing and use of fire). However, compared with forests, grasslands are likely to change more rapidly in the face of climate change or 'inappropriate' human use: increased dryness and/or overgrazing, for example, is known to cause **desertification**, the conversion of grasslands into desert.

Using *WR* pp. 119–131 and the case studies on pp. 212–224 as a source of information, answer Question 3.17.

Question 3.17

What are the three most important factors that have influenced grassland biodiversity?

3.3.5 Interactions between ecosystems

In *WR* the focus is on particular, broadly defined ecosystems. But in reality and from a social and political point of view, what matters are geographical regions with their complex mix of ecosystems. People are concerned about the threats to ecosystems in *their* region and, as many examples in *WR* show, there is a need to understand how ecosystems interact.

Use all the information in *WR* Chapters 2 and 3 to answer Questions 3.18 and 3.19.

Question 3.18

(a) In which types of ecosystem is global climate change thought to be a significant threat in the present or immediate future? (b) What sorts of problem are or may be caused?

Question 3.19

From your study of *WR*, earlier parts of this course and general knowledge, use Table 3.1 to list at least four more examples illustrating how one ecosystem affects one or more others.

Table 3.1

Ecosystem that has an effect	Ecosystem that is affected	Description/example
Forest	Freshwater	Forest ecosystems affect the quality (nutrient and sediment inputs) and quantity of water entering freshwater ecosystems; e.g. New York City watersheds, South African watersheds.

3.4 Further thoughts about ecosystems

WR contains a huge amount of information, collected and analysed by a large body of scientists. In these respects it is better than publications produced by single authors. Nevertheless, *WR* admits to weaknesses in the PAGE approach (considered in Question 3.4) and after your reading of its text, now is a good time to reassess its reliability and breadth of coverage.

First, like any book, *WR* is a snapshot of a field of interest that is constantly changing. In five and certainly ten years after its publication, situations could have changed considerably, especially for the case studies described in Chapter 3.

○ Are changes in the outcomes or predicted outcomes for the case studies likely to be caused by factors within human control or outside it?

● In nearly every case a successful outcome depends more on social or political factors (i.e. under human control) — land ownership, for example — than on external factors beyond human control.

Despite these reservations, the case studies are a valuable source of information about how environmental problems arose and were identified, and what actions were taken to try to remedy the problem. What we do not know is how exceptional these case studies are: have there been many comparable situations where either no action was taken or the actions were ineffective? The case of Cuban agriculture, for example, which you were not directed to study from Chapter 3 but is well worth reading, is probably unique: political forces (the collapse of the former Soviet Union) necessitated a switch from intensive, high-input agriculture to extensive, largely organic farming methods, including much food production within cities. After a difficult start, the switch has been remarkably successful at feeding the Cuban population, due mainly to strong central direction (i.e. top-down control) coupled with a high degree of community involvement and excellent support from Cuban scientists. What will happen in the future should the political situation in Cuba change or if agrochemicals become affordable and available again is anybody's guess.

A second problem, the unreliability of data used in *WR*, is something about which the authors are totally open. They give sources for their data, give copious tables of data on the WRI website, and state clearly when insufficient data were available to draw reliable conclusions. Nevertheless, conclusions are often drawn based on few data and it remains up to the reader to decide whether or not to believe them. An example that illustrates the sort of difficulty faced by PAGE researchers was highlighted in a reassessment of the data for global marine fish catches (Watson and Pauly, 2002). Convincing evidence was presented that the apparently healthy increase in global catches during the 1990s was an artefact caused by massive *over*-reporting from China to the FAO (Food and Agriculture Organization of the UN), which is the only available source of data for global fish catches. Why should this have happened?

> For a number of obvious reasons, fishers usually tend to under-report their catches, and consequently, most countries can be presumed to under-report their catches to FAO, thus we wondered why China should differ from most other countries in this way. We believe that the explanation lies in China's socialist economy, in which the state entities that monitor the economy are also given the

task of increasing its output. Until recently, Chinese officials, at all levels, have tended to be promoted on the basis of production increases from their areas or production units.

(Watson and Pauly, 2002)

The clear implication is that global statistics obtained by summing reports from individual nations can be — for all too human reasons — unreliable and the result can be unjustified complacency (as in the above example) or panic.

The final discussion point is the breadth of coverage in *WR*. We mentioned earlier that their very broad definitions of ecosystem types mean that much variability is smoothed over. However, the open ocean, Earth's largest ecosystem, in terms of both area and or volume, is not covered at all.

○ Can you think of any reasons for this omission?

● *WR* looks at ecosystems as providers of resources or services for people. But nearly all the marine resources (e.g. fish, oil) come from the relatively shallow coastal waters, which are covered in *WR*. From this perspective the open oceans are of only minor importance

However, it would be a serious mistake to think that open oceans do not 'matter'. They are a major carbon sink (Chapter 1) and, together with the atmosphere, play a critical role in regulating Earth's climate and weather patterns. You will learn more about this role in Block 3.

3.4.1 Ecology and climate change

There has also been an increase in knowledge about the impact of climate change on ecosystems and biodiversity since the publication of *WR*, and to bring yourself up-to-date, read the paper Ecological responses to recent climate change (Walther et al., 2002), on the Block 2 Resources CD-ROM.

This paper, written by an international team of scientists and published in one of the leading scientific journals, reviews the impacts of climate change in four areas.

○ What were these four areas?

● (i) Phenology (the timing of seasonal activities) and physiology of organisms; (ii) shifts in the range and distribution of species; (iii) community shifts (changes in composition and interactions); (iv) changes in the structure and complex dynamics of ecosystems.

So the authors considered all levels from individuals to ecosystems in their analysis. One of the most cogent points they make is the great variability in responses of individuals and populations and the difficulty in extrapolating from responses at these levels to responses of communities and ecosystems. They also show the striking variability in local trends of temperature and precipitation change (their Figure 1).

○ In broad terms, where are (a) the main areas of local temperature rise and (b) the main areas of reduced precipitation?

● (a) In the northern hemisphere, mainly at high latitudes. (b) Widely scattered but mostly at mid-latitudes with the three largest areas in central southern Africa, western Asia (Afghanistan, Pakistan) and the central Mediterranean region.

Because organisms respond to their local climate and not to global averages, this climate variability explains some of the observed variability in ecological responses to climate change.

At several places in the paper there are examples of how climate change may have adverse effects on biodiversity.

● List at least three examples of such adverse (or potentially adverse) effects.

● (i) Butterflies respond rapidly to warming by shifting their range but plants (their food sources) respond more slowly. A poor outlook for the butterflies! (ii) Species spread by human intervention may establish and become invasive as a result of climate change. Pathogens and parasites may also spread, a point made in *WR*. (iii) A dramatic increase in plant growth has occurred in Antarctica, with as yet unknown effects on the communities there. (iv) Changes due to coral bleaching, also discussed in *WR*. (v) Potentially adverse effects on reptiles with temperature-controlled sex determination. Several examples showing how responses of one species to climate change may disrupt its interactions with other species. (vi) Altered survival of walleye pollock, affecting the food web in the Bering Sea. (vii) Reduced recruitment of krill, affecting food webs and fishing in the Southern Ocean. (viii) Earlier spawning of newts but not frogs leading to greater predation on frog tadpoles. (ix) Apparently greater susceptibility of mountain frogs to disease in areas of warming. (x) Reduced breeding success of great tits in Europe because a major source of food for nestlings (caterpillars of winter moth) fail to synchronize their growth with the timing of bud-burst in oak.

You may have listed other examples, but there is clearly abundant evidence now that climate change can lead to a wide variety of ecological responses. The fragmented state of many ecosystems now (discussed in *WR*) means that species that cannot adapt to altered climate and have only limited ability to disperse to new, suitable habitats, are more likely than in the geological or even historical past to become extinct. It is becoming increasingly urgent to find answers to the question posed in Section 3.3 'Does declining biodiversity matter?'

Now go to the Web to do the activities associated with this chapter.

3.5 Summary of Chapter 3

3.1 From reading *WR* Chapter 2, you obtained an expert assessment of the state of major ecosystems with respect to their capacity to provide goods and services, including biodiversity, that are important for human welfare. Despite weaknesses in the *WR* approach, it provides the best global assessment so far — but you need to be aware of its limitations.

3.2 The case studies in *WR* Chapter 3 provide examples that illustrate the difficulties of trying to improve damaged ecosystems. For ecosystem remediation, the social and political context becomes dominant, with land ownership and governance of central importance.

3.3 Both top down (e.g. Florida Everglades, Mongolian grasslands) and bottom-up (e.g. Mankòtè, Bolinao, Dhani Forest) approaches have been used in ecosystem renovation projects.

3.4 For coastal ecosystems, as broadly defined in *WR*, the main threats to global biodiversity are conversion, pollution and habitat destruction or damage. The widespread bleaching of coral reefs suggests that they may especially sensitive to climate change.

3.5 Conversion is the main threat to global forest diversity, with disturbance, habitat fragmentation and invasive species as significant secondary threats. The long period of time needed to develop a species-rich forest underlines the importance of conserving ancient forests.

3.6 Freshwater ecosystems are possibly the most crucial for human survival and are also the most vulnerable to damage and the most strongly influenced by other ecosystems. Their biodiversity is in the worst state of all the types of ecosystem assessed in *WR*, with pollution, damage and invasive (alien) species identified as the major threats.

3.7 In grassland ecosystems (broadly defined to include tundra in *WR*), conversion has been the major cause of biodiversity loss, followed by habitat fragmentation and damage or destruction. Desertification is a significant problem, often caused by overuse (e.g. overgrazing) possibly in combination with climate change.

3.8 Just as individuals within species interact, so that a threat to one species may escalate into a threat to many, so ecosystems influence each other. Freshwater ecosystems are affected directly or indirectly by nearly all other types, and the outputs from urban ecosystems similarly affect all others.

3.9 In the longer term the impact of climate change on biodiversity and ecosystems could be the greatest threat of all. Ecological effects at all levels, from individuals to ecosystems, have been identified but it is still too early to attribute any species' extinctions directly to climate change. The higher level impacts (on communities and ecosystems) are especially difficult to determine and quantify.

Learning Outcomes for Chapter 3

When you have completed this chapter you should be able to:

3.1 Define, recognize and use correctly terms shown in **bold** in the text and/or listed in the Glossary.

3.2 Summarize PAGE findings (in *WR*) about the overall condition of four major types of ecosystem and their capacity to deliver goods and services. (Questions 3.1–3.4)

3.3 Analyse the main factors, arising from human activities, that have caused losses of biodiversity and/or affected the functioning of ecosystems, including interactions between ecosystem types. (Questions 3.5–3.7, 3.9–3.13, 3.17–3.19)

3.4 Give examples that illustrate different forms of governance and their role in ecosystem management and restoration. (Questions 3.8, 3.14–3.16)

References

Walther, G. R., Post, E., Convey, P., Menzel, A., Parmesan, C., Beebee, T. J. C., Fromentin, J. M., Hoegh-Guldberg, O. and Bairlein, F. (2002) Ecological responses to recent climate change. *Nature*, **416**, pp. 389–395.

Watson, R. and Pauly, D. (2002) Systematic distortions in world fisheries catch trends. *Nature*, **414**, pp. 534–536.

Chapter 4 Biodiversity in your own backyard

Prepared for the course team by Mike Dodd

4.1 Introduction

This chapter has three sections each looking at a different aspect of biodiversity at the local level. First local biodiversity will be introduced, then we move on to looking at how biodiversity has been measured historically, and finally we will explain the principles involved in measuring biodiversity yourself.

4.2 Biodiversity at the local level

Earlier chapters in this book have concentrated on the big picture of the planet's biodiversity. In this chapter we will be focusing in on local diversity. Most of the examples we discuss are from the UK. However, as you will see, local biodiversity in the UK can affect local diversity in other parts of the world and vice versa. 'Local' can also have different meanings. To the millions of bacteria spending their lives in your gut, local has a quite different meaning to local for the groups of whales migrating round the world's oceans. This idea of scale is very important when considering many different aspects of the environment. In this section, local is used to mean parts of the UK. Later in the chapter you will be focusing in even closer on just the neighbourhood where you live.

Biodiversity is sometimes thought of as a property only of tropical rainforests or coral reefs. Indeed the British overseas territories hold 5500 square kilometres of coral reefs, including some of the most biodiverse areas of the planet. While these ecosystems are very species rich there is also important biodiversity in other parts of the world, including mainland Britain. Two examples of habitats for which the UK has international responsibilities and which contain considerable biodiversity are estuary systems and 'veteran' trees. The estuaries have relatively mild winters and abundant invertebrate populations and, as such, hold huge numbers of over-wintering birds from many other parts of the world. Veteran trees, typified by the gnarled old oaks and beech trees of the New Forest and Windsor Great Park, support a wide range of now very rare insects, lichens and fungi. The UK at present contains 90% of Europe's remaining ancient deciduous trees.

4.2.1 International responsibilities

As with all relatively natural ecosystems in the UK, both estuaries and ancient trees are under considerable development pressure. Estuaries have long been thought of as barren expanses of mud ideal for reclamation, industrial development, tidal barrages, marinas and a whole range of other schemes. However, as any fisherman will tell you, estuary mud is actually very rich in animal life. For example, the young of cockles (*Cerastoderma edule*) can settle at $10\,000\,\text{m}^{-2}$, *Hydrobia* snails can occur at $36\,000\,\text{m}^{-2}$, *Corophium* (shrimp-like organisms) at $22\,000\,\text{m}^{-2}$ and lugworms (*Arenicola marina*) at densities of up to $220\,\text{m}^{-2}$. These organisms all provide food for fish and a wide variety of resident and migrant wading birds. For example, 220 000 knot (*Calidris canutus*) from the high Canadian arctic and Greenland,

Figure 4.1 Massed dunlin landing on a beach at dawn. These birds have travelled thousands of miles from their arctic breeding grounds to over-winter on an ice-free UK estuary.

and 430 000 dunlin (*Calidris alpina*) (Figure 4.1) from Russia and northern Scandinavia rely on just a handful of UK estuaries (Figure 4.2).

When an estuary is modified the type and amount of mud and silt deposited is changed and this in turn alters the range of invertebrates that can live there. Each species of wading bird has a bill shape adapted to feeding on a different range of these invertebrates. Development such as the building of a new marina near the mouth of an estuary may slow down the water flow rate within the estuary and allow more silt to be deposited. This silty layer could cover small rocks used by mussels (*Mytilus edulis*) as an anchor point and so deprive oystercatchers (*Haematopus ostralegus*) of their main food source. This effect is fairly subtle and its casualties would be easy to miss. There will be no heaps of dead birds because they will simply move on, but there are only a limited number of places to which the birds can go and each time they move it costs them vital energy. During their long non-stop migration flight, knot lose 80% of their body fat reserves, so any further movement, especially when they first arrive in Britain, can be fatal.

Figure 4.2 Map showing the main estuaries in the UK.

Over-development of Britain's estuaries also affects biodiversity in other areas of the world. The arctic tundra breeding grounds of knot are still a fairly pristine ecosystem but these birds cannot survive the severe arctic winter and have to rely on flying south to Britain's estuaries. Loss, damage or pollution of these estuaries will affect the bird populations and ultimately the whole food chain on the arctic breeding grounds. Britain's role as an over-wintering destination for birds is currently very important. However, there are suggestions that as the climate warms these over-wintering birds may move from the mild west of Britain to the east coast estuaries as these areas provide better feeding and are more sheltered from the Atlantic gales. Eventually the birds may not come to the UK at all, but over-winter in the low countries, particularly The Netherlands, when these areas become reliably ice free. A regular survey of Britain's estuaries, the Wetland Birds Survey (WeBS), which has been running for many years, is starting to pick up evidence that this west-to-east shift is happening already. It is unclear how the birds would cope with one of the other main predictions of the models of climate change, that of increased year-to-year weather variability.

Perhaps one of the clearest potential cases of irreversible losses of biodiversity involves Britain's ancient trees. If the few remaining groups of ancient trees are removed, as has happened across the rest of Europe, then it will take hundreds of years for new acorns to grow and produce live trees in a suitable state of decay to support all the insects and fungi that depend on today's ancient trees. Research has estimated that the time taken for very species-rich lichen communities to re-establish on ancient trees is at least 200–300 years (Gustafsson et al., 1992). Even existing 100-year-old trees are unlikely to be suitable to take on the role of veterans for a further century or more as these 100-year-old 'youngsters' will not have many of the required habitats such as damaged branches, holes or rotting wood. During the long gap when there is no suitable habitat many of the dependant organisms will probably become extinct. In the UK over 1700 species of invertebrate animals depend on decaying wood to complete their life cycle (Alexander, 1999). Of these, 59% are classed as rare, vulnerable, endangered or may already be extinct, and without veteran trees many of the remaining species will also disappear forever. Some of the species associated with veteran trees include the rather dramatic stag beetle (*Lucanus cervus*) and violet click beetle (*Limoniscus violaceus*), lichens such as *Bacidia incompta*, and the devil's bolete fungus (*Boletus satanas*). Bats including barbastelle *(Barbastella barbastellus)*, Bechstein's (*Myotis bechsteini*), brown long-eared (*Plecotus auritus*) and noctule (*Nyctalus noctula*) all need holes such as those found in old trees for roosting, and glades to forage in. Whole communities of rotting wood (saproxylic) beetles and other invertebrates are thought to be important to the overall health of forests, but many of the individual species have very restricted ranges and are now classed as endangered due to sustained habitat loss. It is remarkable that within just a short distance of London, a major city, the rotting wood within the veteran trees of Windsor Forest and Great Park are home to five species of 'saproxylic' beetle that occur nowhere else. Box 4.1 (overleaf), which you should read now, is a brief history of Britain's veteran trees.

More information on this habitat can be found at the UK Biodiversity Website (2001) where veteran trees come under the classification of lowland wood-pasture and parkland.

4.2.2 Habitat comparisons

Having seen that there are certain very special habitats that Britain has particular responsibility for maintaining, we are now going to look at a couple of the more familiar and widespread habitats in Britain and compare their biodiversity. The comparison is between broadleaved woodland (Figure 4.4) and conifer plantations. Similar habitats occur in many parts of Europe, and although the exact species composition will differ somewhat, the general groups of taxa found will be the same. The comparison between

Box 4.1 How have trees survived to become veterans?

Veteran trees (Figure 4.3) are generally between 300 and 1000 years old. About 1000 years ago, just before the time of the Norman Conquest, much of England was managed as 'wood-pasture'. The Norman aristocracy was very keen on hunting and took large tracts of this newly acquired country as hunting preserves. Some of these areas were declared Royal Forests and commoners and their grazing animals were excluded. It is the remains of these preserves and later deer parks that contain most of today's veteran trees. Elsewhere there was much more pressure to cut trees, as wood was one of the most important resources in people's lives for use as fuel and as the main building material.

Today, the New Forest in Hampshire is the best place to see veteran trees in a woodland setting, but the area could so easily have lost all its mighty trees on several separate occasions in the past. It was declared a Royal Forest in 1079, which meant that it became a place where the king had the right to impose forest laws and keep deer. In the 16th century navy shipyards near to the New Forest used large numbers of oaks from the forest and severely depleted stocks of mature trees. In the early 17th century King James I called a halt to all oak tree and sapling felling in the forest and about 1000 ha of hardwoods were planted. In 1851 the Deer Removal Act reduced the population of deer in the forest — this allowed new trees more chance to grow and increased the area of forest by a further 4047 ha. In 1877 commoners were given the right to pasture their animals in the

forest throughout the year increasing the grazing pressure on trees again. During World War II several level, flat areas of the forest were cleared of all trees to make airfields; these areas subsequently reverted to heather (*Calluna vulgaris*) and gorse (*Ulex* sp.) heathland. After the war the Forestry Commission, charged with the task of maximum timber production, implemented a policy of cutting down all old deciduous woodland and replacing it with conifers. This policy could have destroyed all of the ancient trees but after a public outcry it was halted in 1971. Today, the ancient trees are generally protected. Apart from a very important invertebrate fauna the

ancient trees of the New Forest also support probably the richest epiphytic lichen flora in northwest Europe and some of the richest fungal communities in Europe with over 2600 species having been recorded.

This brief history of the New Forest shows the importance of governance in protecting or destroying biodiversity. It was the government of the time that instructed the Forestry Commission to deliberately cut down an ancient biodiverse ecosystem that had taken thousands of years to form. At the last moment it was intervention by the public that saved the remaining forest fragments, by protest on the streets and via other unofficial channels.

Figure 4.3 An example of a veteran tree — an oak (*Quercus robur*).

these two habitats helps us to visualize the differences between a relatively species-rich and a species-poor ecosystem. It also shows the reasons why the two types of habitat, which are after all both woodland, should vary so much in their biodiversity.

In the Countryside Survey (2000), which you can view on the web, broadleaved, mixed and yew woodlands are all grouped together as one broad habitat type. It is this group that will be compared with coniferous plantations. Each habitat type covers about 1.5×10^6 ha, 6% of the total land area of the UK.

Figure 4.4 Broadleaved woodland showing some of the main species and niches.

Broadleaved woodland

Figure 4.5 shows a phylogenetic outline of some of the groups of organisms found in broadleaved woodland.

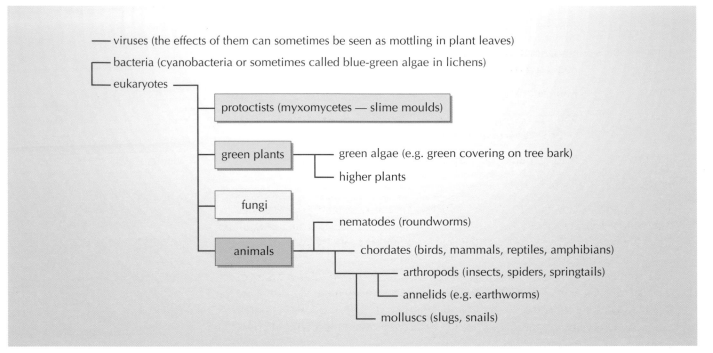

Figure 4.5 Phylogenetic outline of some of the groups of organisms found in broadleaved woodland.

Activity 4.1   Woodland biodiversity

On the copy of Figure 4.5 below, write the names of the organisms shown in Figure 4.4 in their correct positions on the outline.

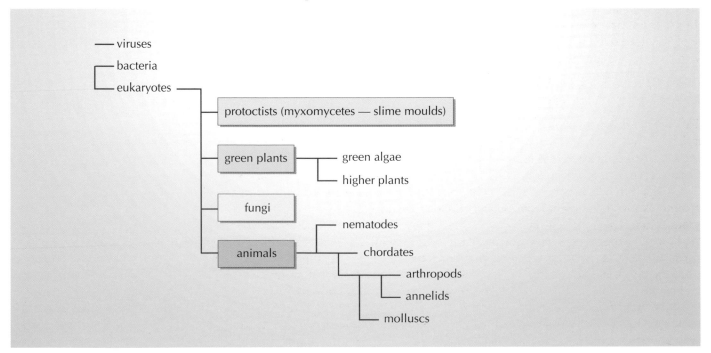

Comment

The list below shows where the organisms should be placed on the outline:

bacteria	cyanobacteria (blue-green algae) within lichen
green algae	algae on tree trunk
higher plants	beech tree; oak tree; foxglove; broad buckler fern; dog violet; sedge; brambles
fungi	beefsteak fungus; sulphur tuft
chordates	toad; grass snake; chaffinch; green woodpecker; badger; noctule bat; wood mouse; roe deer;
arthropods	fritillary butterfly; purple hairstreak butterfly; stag beetle
mollusc	slug

If you happen to compare Figure 4.5 with the Tree of Life (2002) website that we encountered earlier you will see that many of the intermediate branches and taxa have been removed, leaving just the main groups that can be seen in a British woodland. For example, groups such as the Rhodophyta (the red seaweeds) have been removed since you do not normally find seaweeds in woodland. Many of the very small organisms within the protoctists have also been omitted as they are too small to be seen with the naked eye during a walk in the woods, although of course they are still important elements of the biodiversity occurring there.

Conifer plantations

Detailed comparison of the difference in biodiversity between the broadleaved woodland outlined above and a conifer plantation (Figure 4.6, overleaf) is not straightforward, as no single person has the time or expertise to study in detail the diversity of all the different groups of woodland creatures shown in Figure 4.4. There has also been a tendency for ecologists in Britain to take an interest in broadleaved woodlands with very few researchers examining the diversity of species within conifer plantations.

What might be the cause of the difference in the amount of biodiversity seen in native broadleaved woodland and conifer plantations?

The main tree species grown in conifer plantations are: Norway spruce (*Picea abies*), hybrid larch (*Larix x eurolepis*), Sitka spruce (*Picea sitchensis*), grand fir (*Abies grandis*), western red cedar (*Thuja plicata*), lodgepole pine (*Pinus contorta*), Corsican pine (*Pinus nigra*), Douglas fir (*Pseudotsuga menziesii*) and western hemlock (*Tsuga heterophylla*). None of these conifers is native to Britain. Each type of tree is commonly planted as a single species block and grown as a crop to maximize its wood production. There are normally very few other plant species growing within the blocks, perhaps just a few scattered ferns and mosses. The reason for this is that when the trees are recently planted, herbicides are often used to suppress all other plant species. Later, as the tree canopy develops, the light intensity at ground level is reduced to very low levels throughout the year, typically less than 10% of incident light under Sitka spruce in northern Britain (Hale, 2001). Even species such as bluebells that manage to survive in dense broadleaved woodland by growing early in the year before leaves form on the trees cannot survive a dark year-round canopy. A reduction in plant species diversity generally causes a reduction in all other groups of organisms as they all ultimately depend on plants to capture the Sun's energy and turn it into food or shelter. For example, there are unlikely to be any of the 284 species of insects associated with oak in a western hemlock plantation. In comparison only 37 species of insect depend on Sitka spruce and 17 species depend on non-native larch.

Figure 4.6 A conifer plantation showing some of the main species and niches.

Fahy and Gormally (1998) carried out one of the few studies comparing a semi-natural oak woodland and a nearby mature Sitka spruce conifer plantation in Ireland. They found significantly more species of plant — an average of 16.5 per 2 m × 2 m quadrat — in the oak woodland compared with an average of just 6.5 species per quadrat in the conifer plantation. They also found three times as many species and many more individuals of carabid beetles in the oak woodland compared to the plantation.

The explanation for this difference is that native species of plants and animals have evolved together and migrated with each other into the British Isles since the end of the last ice age. Insects native to Britain feed on British trees whereas many of the invertebrates that would normally feed on the introduced conifers have either been left behind in their native region or do not survive under British conditions. However, there are exceptions, such as the native winter moth that attacks Sitka spruce in Scotland. The distinction between native and introduced species can sometimes prove confusing if you consider that 10 000 years ago ice-sheets covered most of the British Isles and much of the current flora and fauna had retreated further south. When conditions warmed up the flora and fauna slowly came back en masse, so preserving many of the close ecological linkages between species distributions. When non-native species are introduced nowadays, for example as garden plants or to be grown in plantations, then it is without all the other components of their native ecosystems. As you have already seen in Chapters 2 and 3, taking a species from one part of the world and introducing it into another can cause all sorts of unforeseen consequences. Once released from the predators keeping it in check in its native ecosystem the species may spread to become a major pest in its new home. For example, giant hogweed (*Heracleum mantegazzianum*), a plant with huge leaves, was originally introduced from southwest Asia and grown as an 'architectural' plant in gardens. Now it is widespread along railway embankments, roadsides and river banks in many parts of Europe. Not only does it displace native vegetation it causes severe rashes if the sap comes into contact with skin and the skin is exposed to sunlight.

It is not only animal and plant diversity that is reduced in conifer plantations. Several authors (Burova, 1974; Villeneuve et al., 1989; Ferris et al., 2000) have shown that the numbers of important mycorrhizal fungi species are also positively correlated with plant species diversity. Mycorrhizal fungi are particularly important as they facilitate the growth of most species of trees and other plants. Interestingly, Humphrey et al. (2000) suggests that a number of these mycorrhizal species of fungi are starting to shift from native Caledonian pine forest into the conifer plantations of northern Britain.

4.3 How biodiversity has been measured in the UK

Glancing up from this book and looking outside you may see a variety of different plants and animals. In the previous chapter we discussed many aspects of global biodiversity; we are now going to show how some familiar native organisms can be used to assess biodiversity at a local level.

Since Victorian times, or even earlier, keen amateur naturalists have been recording species in the UK (see Box 4.2, overleaf). From the middle of the 20th century organizations such as the Botanical Society of the British Isles (BSBI) and the British Trust for Ornithology started to coordinate this recording. They also provided lists of experts who specialized in taxa that were particularly difficult to identify. These organizations currently ensure that there is one individual responsible for collating the records from each county and then sending them on to the national database. The Biological Records Centre (BRC, 2002) contains many of these records. You may want to visit their website and select 'data holdings' to get an idea of the millions of records and wide taxonomic coverage. In the data holdings there are large numbers of records from such groups as vascular plants, mosses and liverworts, slugs and snails, butterflies, fish and mammals, each of which has a dedicated group of people who have been recording species over many years. Not all records are kept at the BRC, for example the records for birds and most fungi are kept elsewhere.

BSBI and societies for other groups of organisms try to achieve complete mapping of the whole country at a scale of 10 km × 10 km (one hectad) or finer detail, indicating whether or not each species of plant is present in each of these grid squares.

Box 4.2 *The Natural History of Selborne*

Figure 4.7 The amateur naturalist Gilbert White (1720–1793)

Gilbert White (Figure 4.7) was one of the best known of the early amateur naturalists largely due to the success of his book *The Natural History of Selborne*. The book consists of a series of letters, in which he made many original contributions to science and nature. In 1768 he wrote:

> I wonder that the stone curlew, charadrius oedicnemus, should be mentioned by the writers as a rare bird: it abounds in all the campaign parts of Hampshire and Sussex, and breeds, I think, all the summer, having young ones, I know, very late in the autumn. Already they begin clamouring in the evening. They cannot, I think, with any propriety, be called, as they are by Mr. Ray, 'circa aquas versantes' [around running water]; for with us, by day at least, they haunt only the most dry, open, upland fields and sheep walks, far removed from water. What they may do in the night I cannot say. Worms are their usual food, but they also eat toads and frogs.

> I can show you some good specimens of my new mice. Linnaeus, perhaps, would call the species mus minimus.

> (From Letter XV, to Thomas Pennant Esquire, March 30 1768)

The stone curlew (now known as *Burhinus oedicnemus*) is now extremely rare and Gilbert White was the first person to identify the harvest mouse (now known as *Micromys minutus*), which he described more extensively in other letters.

The full text of the book is freely available on the Web from Project Gutenberg (2002). The downloaded book contains some copyright notices then the full text. This classic book gives an account of the natural history of part of Hampshire but it also contains much more, for example about the geology and people of the area. The text is searchable, so if you load it into a word processor, you could find, for example, all the references to eels or see if primroses are mentioned at all. You could also check to see, for example, what White says about birds such as the swallow (*Hirundo rustica*) which we now know migrate south to over-winter in Africa, but at that time were generally thought to hibernate in a range of unlikely places.

Individual recorders visit their grid squares several times during the season so that plants that are only visible for short periods are not missed. Achieving good coverage of a grid square usually takes several years since each square is large and contains many kilometres of footpaths and a variety of habitats. Coverage of the whole of the UK is a huge task — the distance from the south coast of Cornwall to the north of Scotland is well over 900 km, an area of 244 820 km^2 giving about 3500 hectads. Yet these amateur groups have managed to carry out complete surveys on at least two occasions during the 20th century. Britain probably has the best record of species distributions anywhere in the world, due largely to these very dedicated naturalists. Indeed one of the main points highlighted at a workshop on strategies for conserving biodiversity was 'the need for the enthusiasm and interests of amateurs to be trained, directed and supported [in biological recording]'(Flemming et al., 1997).

It is too expensive for the government to provide this very detailed complete coverage of the whole of the UK but it does carry out representative random sampling programmes such as the Countryside Survey. This survey uses detailed field observations from a random sample of 1 km grid squares combined with satellite images to produce a land cover map for the whole country as well as reports on each habitat type.

Figure 4.8 Pennyroyal (*Mentha pulegium*).

In many other parts of the world species distributions are recorded by 'professionals' rather than amateurs. If you are a student from outside the UK then try to find out how biodiversity is monitored in your country.

As soon as species distributions have been mapped more than once it is possible to gain an idea of change over time. A botanist noting down plants 50 years ago probably had little notion of the concept of biodiversity as we understand it today, but those records now give a very good idea of the amount of diversity loss across the country when compared with recent surveys.

For example, pennyroyal (*Mentha pulegium*) (Figure 4.8) was a widespread species found in 126 grid squares before 1930. Between 1930 and 1970 it was found in only 43 squares and it is now classed as rare, having been found in only 15 squares between 1980 and 1994 (Stewart et al., 1994).

Focusing down from national level, imagine you wanted to measure biodiversity in your local area. How would you set about doing this?

At first this might sound like an impossible task since biodiversity covers all living organisms from bacteria to bats. However, you may be able to get an idea of the level of biodiversity by measuring just one group of organisms. Native higher plants are often chosen as the first group to look at since they are readily found, good identification guides are available, and there are usually local experts if you need help. Plants are a good group to choose from an ecological point of view because of their fundamental role in ecosystems (Chapter 1). Diversity in your local area can also be related to diversity at the national scale since there have been many surveys done of other parts of the country. Of course individual species of plants support different species of insect so, for example, if nettles are not present in your local area then there will be no small tortoiseshell butterfly (*Aglais urticae*) caterpillars.

Now go to the website to do the activities associated with this part of the chapter.

4.4 'Hands-on' biodiversity recording and statistical analysis

4.4.1 Species surveys

The group of species chosen for a biodiversity survey will differ depending on the objective. For example, if you wanted to look at change in distribution patterns over time then recording just the presence/absence in grid squares would enable you to compare distribution maps drawn at each time interval. However, if you also wanted your survey to use the taxa as biological indicators to detect changing environmental conditions then the group of species used would need to be carefully thought out. Generally, increasing the number of species in the group of interest also increases the types of information that can be obtained from the final data, but the species would need to be relatively straightforward to find and identify otherwise the recording could be very difficult or unreliable. Flowering plants are often used in surveys for this very reason: there are about 1500 species in the UK and any competent botanist should be able to identify them all.

A typical plant survey would not only give an idea of the botanical biodiversity of an area, but potentially it could also give a considerable amount of information on the habitats, soil type, disturbance and climate. For example, if a survey using 2 m × 2 m quadrats found an area completely dominated by perennial ryegrass (*Lolium perenne*) and clover (*Trifolium* sp.) then it is likely to be a pasture grazed and/ or cut each year and on fairly rich fertilized soil. However, if a similar survey found 50 species including those such as salad burnet (*Sanguisorba minor*), glaucous sedge (*Carex glauca*), wild thyme (*Thymus polytrichus*) and small scabious (*Scabiosa columbaria*) in the same size quadrats then it is likely to be a dry limestone grassland with short grazed turf on poor thin soil. Thus the most basic result from a survey such as this is that one site has low diversity (two species) and the other has high diversity (50 species). However, the survey contains much more information than this; as many plants are restricted in where they can grow, if we know about the ecology of each species it is possible to predict the habitat conditions at the survey site. If a resurvey of these sites is carried out and a significant change is detected then it is likely that the cause of the change could also be deduced. For example, an increase in the number of species on the pasture probably results from reduced fertilizer input. A change towards more shrub or tree species on the limestone grassland might suggest a reduction in grazing, perhaps as a result of the disease myxomatosis eradicating the rabbit population in that area.

Biodiversity surveys of other groups of organisms such as dragonflies (Odonata) contain less of this additional ecological information as there are a lot fewer species within this group. Even so, they can still offer some information about the habitat. For example, if certain species such as the white-legged damselfly (*Platycnemis pennipes*) (Figure 4.9) are present in rivers in central and southern England then it indicates that the watercourse is not heavily polluted.

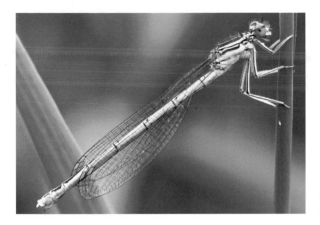

Figure 4.9 White-legged damselfly (*Platycnemis pennipes*).

4.4.2 Collecting and analysing biodiversity data

Recall that in Book 1, Section 4.5 you used a stepwise process to answer questions using the Web.

○ What were the steps in this process?

● **A** Define your question; **B** think about what you will need to answer it; **C** go to the Internet to seek the information you require; **D** evaluate and analyse the information; **E** draw your conclusions; **F** possibly update your question and repeat steps A–F as necessary (Book 1, Figure 4.7).

Scientific investigations follow a very similar procedure. You start with a question that may arise from casual observation. For example, while out walking you may notice that warmer parts of the country seem to contain more dragonfly species than cooler regions. To investigate this further you must frame the observation in the form of a **hypothesis**, which can be tested. The hypothesis might be that dragonfly diversity and temperature positively vary in parallel with one another (i.e. high dragonfly diversity is associated with high temperatures and low diversity with low temperatures). Next, you need to decide what data need to be collected to test your hypothesis. For example, numbers of dragonflies and local temperatures could be measured at, say, seven locations across Britain. This raises all kinds of questions about *how* the data should be collected, such as precisely when dragonfly numbers will be counted and over what period of time and temperature. These details about how data will be collected are described as your **sampling strategy**. There are some similarities here with designing strategies for searching the web, though the analogy shouldn't be pushed too far. *Data collection* itself is, of course, a vital step, not unlike trawling the web. Having collected your data, you need to *analyse* them. This is the equivalent of the 'evaluation' stage in web research and it involves checking whether the relationship predicted by your hypothesis really exists. This step is an important stage of the investigation and we shall return to it below. For the moment, let's imagine that you have found that dragonfly numbers and temperature *do* vary with one another. This result will lead to the *conclusion* that your hypothesis is supported, but you will probably not want to leave it there. You will probably now want to *refine* your question and ask *why* there is a relationship between the two quantities that you have measured. At this point you will formulate a new hypothesis and go around the loop again.

● Summarize the stages of a scientific investigation that have just been described.

● **A** Formulate a hypothesis; **B** design a sampling strategy for data collection; **C** collect the data; **D** analyse the data; **E** draw your conclusions, **F** refine your hypothesis or create a new one and go back to step A.

We shall now look at two of these stages in a bit more detail.

4.4.3 The hypothesis

The initial observation was that there are more dragonfly species in areas with a warmer climate. Such a hypothesis only predicts that there should be 'more' species but does not give any specific figures, making it difficult to test directly. One way of testing whether a relationship does exist is to set up a '**null hypothesis**', which in this case might be that there is no (null) difference in the number of species across the range of temperatures. It is now possible to carry out a suitable statistical test to see how likely it is that the null hypothesis is true. If it is very unlikely that the null hypothesis is true then we may reject it and instead decide that the data do really show some kind of relationship between species diversity and temperature.

Before carrying out any data analysis (indeed even before collecting the data!) it is important to think about the question we are attempting to answer and to devise a suitable null hypothesis. Think back to ideas of biodiversity hotspots in Chapter 3 and assume you are planning to organize a survey of the UK to look at biodiversity using the three groups of organisms — dragonflies, birds and woodlice. One of the questions might be: 'Do parts of the country with the most dragonfly species also have large numbers of bird and woodlice species?' You could frame this question as the hypothesis that there is a correlation between the number of dragonfly species and the number of bird and woodlice species. In general terms this is known as the **overlapping hotspots hypothesis**.

● What would the correct null hypothesis be in this case?

● No correlation exists between the number of dragonfly species and the number of bird and woodlice species.

If we can reject this null hypothesis the result could be potentially very important. That is, if a correlation does exist and there are just a few areas containing high biodiversity, as measured by all groups of species, then it might be possible to protect a large number of species by concentrating resources upon the protection of a limited number of hotspots. This is a strategy that Conservation International advocates on a global scale. Would it work more locally, in the British Isles?

4.4.4 Waves on a beach and probability

Once we have collected and analysed our data, we shall need to decide how likely it is that the result we have obtained might be due to chance. There is no such thing as certainty in science, but some results have such a low **probability** of being due to chance that we treat them as genuine. Strictly speaking, the null hypothesis (e.g. that no relationship exists) is rejected with a specified level of confidence, or **significance level**. This value is usually measured as a percentage such as 95% or 99%, i.e. we are 95% or 99% confident that the hypothesis can be rejected. The confidence level is never 100%!

We all estimate probabilities during everyday life without really thinking about it. What is the chance of being hit by a car if I cross the road here? Would it be better to move further away from the roundabout so there is more chance of seeing the cars coming at me? In cases such as these we estimate the probability and risk to ourselves all in one and make an instant decision about how to act. We usually incorporate a wide margin for error in the original probability estimate since the risk to ourselves is so high.

In other cases it is more difficult to estimate the probability, especially when there is a lot of variation involved. For example, imagine you are standing on a beach on a stormy day. How do you know if the tide is coming in or going out? Most likely there will be large waves and small waves and you might advance down the beach a little way after a series of small waves only to get your feet wet when a sudden large wave comes crashing in (Figure 4.10). Ecological data are very often like this — there is a lot of short-term variability such as that shown by the waves but there may also be an important underlying signal — in this case, the tide coming in.

In the seaside example it would actually be fairly easy to detect which way the tide was going. All you would need to do is push a stick into the sand and wait half an hour to see, on average, if the sea had completely covered the stick or not. But how would you detect overall sea level change on that beach, perhaps due to global warming? This would require careful measurements of sea level over many years, to enable a graph of change in sea level over time to be drawn. However, it is possible that all this graph would show is the variability caused by tides and storms, etc. The small (but real and important) overall change in average sea level would probably be missed.

Figure 4.10 Waves on a beach.

At this point statistics come in (Box 4.3, overleaf). There are mathematical methods of cutting through the variability and getting at underlying trends to say how likely the trends are to be real and not just the result of random chance. In the seaside example there are various complex cycles involved as well as random variation and there are statistical ways of dealing with this type of information — to examine the cycles themselves or to remove them and look at underlying trends. We are only going to concentrate on simple linear trends, as these relationships are usually the best place to start when dealing with ecological systems. You might question why you need to be able to carry out statistical analysis. One of the main aims of this course is to equip you with the ability to make sense of the environmental web yourself. There is no shortage of claims and counter-claims on the bigger environmental issues on the Web, but one of the major advantages of the medium is that it is often possible to actually find the underlying data on which the claims are based, if you look hard enough. It is then possible to carry out your own analysis. Perhaps a claim is simply wrong or, perhaps more likely, the proponents have been highly selective in their use of the data. It is only by going through the process of collecting data yourself and statistically analysing it that you can see all the inherent difficulties in the process and learn to appreciate how others may have overcome these problems. We will give you an insight into this process by doing some simple analyses here, though it is beyond the scope of the course to teach the methods that would be required to analyse more complicated data.

Box 4.3 From uncertainty to probability

You should, by now, be well acquainted with uncertainty as a theme of this course. One type of uncertainty arises from the variability found in nature. Will the next wave on the beach be a small one, or will I get soaked? In order to tame such uncertainties, gain knowledge about them and use that knowledge to understand environmental processes we must *quantify* them. Imagine you are sitting near the sea on a Mediterranean beach. There are no tides in the Mediterranean, so the sea is not creeping towards or away from you. Your chance of getting wet depends upon just three measurable quantities.

◔ What are these quantities?

◑ 1 Your distance from the sea; 2 how frequent the waves big enough to reach you are; 3 how long you sit there.

If you can be troubled to make these measurements when next you find yourself on a suitable beach, you can use the data to predict the probability that someone sitting in the same spot, for say an hour, in similar wind conditions will get wet.

Anything else that varies in some measurable way can be assigned a probability in a similar way, as long as you have enough observations to measure accurately how much variation there is. One standard method for recording variation is to draw a bar chart of the frequency with which measurements of a particular size have been recorded.

◔ You have already drawn such a bar chart in Chapter 1 of this book. What did it show?

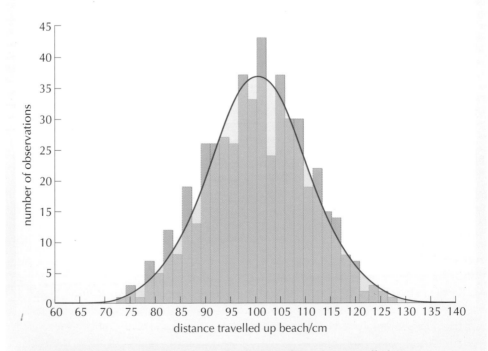

Figure 4.11 Frequency distribution for the distance that waves travelled up a Mediterranean beach.

In Activity 2.1 you plotted the frequency (once, twice, etc.) with which species turned up in foods. Most species were found in only one food, and only a few species occurred in many (Figure 1.17).

A chart such as Figure 1.17 is called a **frequency distribution**. Figure 4.11 shows a frequency distribution for the distance that waves travelled up an imaginary Mediterranean beach from a marker driven into the sand. It indicates that the most common distance travelled was 100 cm, but there was a good deal of variation and a few waves reached much longer or shorter distances than this. Randomly varying measurements often have a frequency distribution like the bell-shaped curve shown in Figure 4.11, which is known as a **normal distribution**. The precise shape of the normal curve is controlled by two parameters, the **mean**, which determines where the peak of the curve is, and the **standard deviation** which determines how spread out the tails are. Both can be calculated from raw data.

Once the shape of the distribution is established then it is possible to divide up the area under the curve (Figure 4.12) according to the number of observations, which fall in each section. For any normally distributed variable it turns out that half of all the measurements lie close to the mean, which for our waves is within the limits of 93.2 and 106.8 cm. In a similar way it is possible to predict the distance limits that would cover 95 or 99% of all waves. This is how, in principle, statistical probabilities are worked out. In short, it is assumed that the data are drawn from a distribution (often, but not always, the normal distribution) and probabilities are then calculated from that. For example, the probability of a wave of 102 cm is greater than 50% so if you stood at 102 cm then your feet would get wet almost immediately but if you stood at 130 cm on this calm Mediterranean shore only rare large waves (less than 1% of all waves) would reach you.

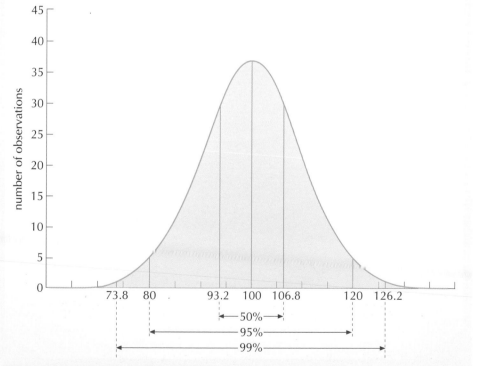

Figure 4.12 A normal distribution curve.

Two of the more common statistical analyses are correlation analysis and simple linear regression. These two types of analysis are rather similar and can be confused. Correlation analysis looks at whether two sets of numbers (variables) change together. One variable may *cause* the other to change but the analysis does not assume this. Correlation does not prove causation: the two sets of figures could be completely independent of each other. For example, we could correlate the number of dragonfly species with say the number of satellite dishes. The analysis simply asks how closely the sets of figures vary together and the result is a single number — the **correlation coefficient**. However, in **regression** analysis one variable y depends on an independent variable x and we aim to carefully describe this relationship so that if necessary we could predict values of y given values of x. The result in this case is an equation linking the two variables and a significance level.

4.4.5 Correlation

Table 4.1 gives an example of some data on how the numbers of three groups of species vary with distance north in the UK. The table of correlation coefficients (Table 4.2) shows how closely the three variables (numbers of bird, dragonfly and woodlice species shown in Table 4.1) are related to each other. A value of 1 indicates a perfect correlation and a very small number shows there is very little linear relationship between the variables. The variables can also be either positively or negatively related to each other. For example, birds and woodlice have a correlation coefficient of −0.94 indicating that they are negatively related, that is, as the number of birds increases, the number of woodlice decreases, or vice versa. But how 'significant' is this value? If more data had been collected might the value have changed to +0.94?

Table 4.1 Some sample data showing how the numbers of British bird, dragonfly and woodlouse species change with the distance north. These data are for illustration only; normally you would need substantially more data than this before carrying out a correlation analysis. Distance north figures are explained in the section on geographical grid systems (Section 4.4.7).

Grid square	Distance north	Number of bird species	Number of dragonfly species	Number of woodlouse species
1	400000	10	5	1
2	500000	5	3	2
3	600000	3	8	3
4	700000	2	4	4

Table 4.2 Correlation coefficients calculated from the data in Table 4.1.

	Birds	Dragonflies	Woodlice
Birds	1		
Dragonflies	−0.13	1	
Woodlice	−0.94	0.12	1

When carrying out any kind of statistical test such as correlation or regression it is usual to say what the probability is of getting results at least this extreme, given that the null hypothesis is true. If the probability of getting these results is low then it is likely that you have found a real effect. To find the significance (or probability) level of the correlation coefficients shown in Table 4.2 it is necessary to consult a set of statistical tables — an example is shown in Table 4.3.

The second row of the correlation coefficient table shows the significance level (5% or 1%). The first column shows *n*, the number of observations in the analysis (in this example the number of grid squares). To use the tables look down the first column until you find the number of grid squares for which data have been collected, then look across the table to the second column and write down the number that you find there. If the absolute value (i.e. the number ignoring the plus or minus) of the correlation coefficient is higher than this then the value is significant at the 5% level — this is sometimes denoted by a single asterisk *. Moving across the table it is also possible to note whether the correlation is significant at the 1% level or less, denoted by **. If you are using a spreadsheet to calculate correlations the program itself may directly give the significance level of the correlation coefficients but it is still a good idea to look at the statistical tables as they clearly show how the significance level changes with increased numbers of observations.

- Do the values of the correlation coefficients in Table 4.3 change evenly with the number of observations?

- No, with a small total number of observations each additional record has a large effect on the value in the table whereas with a large number of observations, additional observations have only a slight effect on the critical value in the table.

Knowing how these critical values change helps to plan how many observations should be collected. For example, if you only have four records then collecting a further four records will have a large effect on the critical value and thus the chance of obtaining a significant result. On the other hand, if you already have 1000 records then four more will have virtually no effect.

When dealing with ecological experiments and surveys such as the one described above, results are usually considered significant if they are likely to occur by chance with a probability of less than one in twenty, called the 5% level of significance. In other instances such as medical trials, where it is absolutely vital that the effect must be real, then a 0.1% level of significance might be used so only correlations with a significance level of 0.999 or higher would be considered. It is perhaps worth emphasizing again here that even with a very highly significant result, it is still possible (although very unlikely) that this effect occurred by chance. In our example described above there is a chance (however small) that the number of satellite dishes is highly significantly correlated with the number of dragonfly species, but from our background ecological knowledge we would just say this was just a fluke. However, if we found that the number of bird and dragonfly species was significantly correlated, then there may well be something interesting going on that is worth further investigation.

- Using Table 4.3 find out the significance levels of the three correlation coefficients given in Table 4.2.

- In the case of the correlation coefficients shown in Table 4.2 it turns out that none of the correlation coefficients are significant (this would be denoted by 'ns' for not significant) even though values of the correlation coefficients themselves are high. The reason for this is that there are so few data in Table 4.2 — only four grid squares have been monitored.

Table 4.3 Statistical table of correlation coefficients for determining significance levels. '2-sided' means that the values can be either positively or negatively related to each other.

n	P (2-sided) 5%	1%
3	0.9969	0.9999
4	0.9500	0.9900
5	0.8783	0.9587
6	0.8114	0.9172
7	0.7545	0.8745
8	0.7067	0.8343
9	0.6664	0.7977
10	0.6319	0.7646
20	0.4438	0.5614
30	0.3610	0.4629
40	0.3120	0.4026
50	0.2787	0.3610
100	0.1966	0.2565
200	0.1388	0.1818
300	0.1133	0.1485
400	0.0981	0.1287
500	0.0877	0.1151
1000	0.0620	0.0814
2000	0.0438	0.0576
3000	0.0358	0.0470
4000	0.0310	0.0407

It would, therefore, be very easy to jump to the wrong conclusions if just the correlation coefficients were presented without the significance levels.

4.4.6 Testing the species–energy hypothesis using regression

In this course there has been a considerable amount of material on biodiversity and how it varies from place to place. One theory (of many) to explain why biodiversity varies is called the energy hypothesis, which states that areas with more energy have more species. James H. Brown in 1981 (Brown, 1981) proposed what has become known as the '**species–energy hypothesis**' to explain the considerable decline in number of species between the Equator and the Poles. The hypothesis predicts that the number of species will be related to the amount of available solar energy, usually measured by temperature and sunshine hours. All organisms need to find enough energy (food) to survive and produce offspring; the more energy there is, the more organisms and hence more species the environment can support. This is only one of several different hypotheses to account for the variation in biodiversity, all of which are controversial to some degree and none of which are fully proven.

Table 4.4 Statistical table of regression coefficients for determining significance levels.

n	P (2-sided)	
	5%	1%
3	12.7062	63.6559
4	4.3027	9.9250
5	3.1824	5.8408
6	2.7765	4.6041
7	2.5706	4.0321
8	2.4469	3.7074
9	2.3646	3.4995
10	2.3060	3.3554
20	2.1009	2.8784
30	2.0484	2.7633
40	2.0244	2.7116
50	2.0106	2.6822
100	1.9845	2.6269
200	1.9720	2.6009
300	1.9680	2.5924
400	1.9659	2.5882
500	1.9647	2.5857
1000	1.9623	2.5808
2000	1.9612	2.5783
3000	1.9608	2.5775
4000	1.9606	2.5771

● Assuming there has been a large survey recording the number of species in each 10 km grid square of the UK, how could the energy hypothesis be tested using these data?

● One way of looking at this hypothesis with the data collected is to assume that there is a temperature (and so energy) gradient from south to north in the UK (the north being colder). With a large survey there will be information on the number of species from right along this gradient. It would then be possible to investigate if the number of species decreases from south to north. A first step might be to plot the information on a graph with the distance north along the bottom axis and the number of species found along the vertical axis. Just looking at the scatter of points might give the first hint as to whether there was indeed a relationship between the amount of solar energy and number of species but it would need to be tested statistically.

A range of more sophisticated analyses is also possible, especially if climate and other environmental factors are known for each grid square.

A type of statistical analysis called simple linear regression may help to test the energy hypothesis. This technique allows a straight line to be drawn that best fits the data points. It also indicates just how well the line actually fits and what the significance level of the fit is. As with correlation coefficients the significance level can be determined from statistical tables (Table 4.4). In the survey example mentioned above there is an independent variable — temperature (indicated by distance north), which may cause changes in a dependent variable — the number of species. Regression analysis would show if there is a significant linear relationship between temperature and species diversity and allow prediction of the number of species for any given temperature.

Figure 4.13 shows a graph representing the results of a regression analysis. Each grid square where the number of species has been counted will have a value on the horizontal (x) axis equal to its distance north. Squares near Edinburgh will be further to the right-hand side than squares near London. The vertical (y) axis represents the number of species recorded in each square. The line (regression line) on the graph shows what the underlying relationship between the number of species and distance north might look like. The individual points representing each 10 km square are not shown on the graph.

The regression line has an equation of the form $y = mx + c$, where m is the slope of the line and c is the intercept. The intercept in this case is the point where the regression line cuts (intercepts) the y axis, it indicates the number of species to be found where the distance north is zero. The regression equation allows estimation of the number of species (y) for any distance north (x) — simply substitute the values for 'm' and 'c' from the regression graph back into the equation and choose a distance north.

As an example, say we wanted to know how many species we could expect to find in a grid square at 500000 north. Assuming that from the regression analysis $m = -0.00001$ and $c = 20$ (m is negative because the line slopes down indicating there are fewer species further north). Using the equation $y = mx + c$:

$$y = (-0.00001 \times 500000) + 20$$

$$y = 15,$$ that is there are 15 species in the grid square at 500000 north.

● How many species would you expect in a grid square at 400000 north?

● 16: [$y = (-0.00001 \times 400000) + 20$]

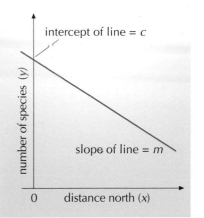

Figure 4.13 Number of species vs distance north, showing a regression line.

4.4.7 Geographical grid systems

The large numbers we are dealing with here such as 500000 arise as a result of the example being based on the GB Ordnance Survey (OS) grid. The number 500000 means 500 000 metres further north than the arbitrary zero point that the OS has chosen which is just south of the Scilly Isles. Grid line 400000 is simply 100 km (or 100 000 metres) further south than 500 000. More information on the OS grid is given on their website (Ordnance Survey, 2002).

If the distance north axis were converted from the OS grid to the worldwide degrees latitude/longitude grid then theoretically the whole world could be included on the same graph. Latitude zero would be the Equator and the intercept with the y axis would then give an estimate of the maximum number of species in that group that it is possible to have on Earth.

● Do you think it would be a good idea to use the information collected from the UK to predict the number of species at the Equator?

● Although it is possible to collect data and test to see if the energy hypothesis is supported over the range of latitudes in the UK, it is incorrect to expect exactly the same relationship between latitude and diversity to hold for all other places on Earth. The UK is a relatively small intensively cultivated part of the world and the range of habitats in other parts of the world is much greater than in the UK. The further you go from the region where the data were collected the larger the error is likely to be. To predict the number of species at the Equator and indeed to test the energy hypothesis more thoroughly data would need to be collected over a wider range of latitudes, particularly from more tropical areas.

● If you were to collect your own data and produce your own version of Figure 4.13 do you think there will be the very obvious straight line relationship indicated in this figure, even if the species–energy hypothesis is true?

It is unlikely. There are many possible factors that could affect the number of species recorded at each location, including:

- errors made by the recorder
- habitat differences not associated with temperature; for example, sampling on acid compared to alkali soil types
- differences in elevation: a habitat recorded high up in the English Peak District may have a temperature equivalent to a similar habitat much further north at sea level
- random day to day fluctuations in weather, more species being recorded on a particularly fine day

You may be able to think of many other factors that could affect the individual records; the question is whether this 'noise' will completely obscure any underlying pattern, assuming there is a pattern to find.

As we have seen earlier, in the environmental sciences the raw data are frequently complex with many different factors involved. It is therefore vital to be able to carry out statistical analysis to find underlying patterns and significance in the data.

You should now go to the Web and complete the activities associated with this chapter.

4.5 Summary of Chapter 4

4.1   Biodiversity is present on the local scale within the UK as well as in areas commonly associated with biodiversity such as rainforests or coral reefs.

4.2   There are certain habitats and species that the UK has particular international responsibilities to protect. These include veteran trees and estuaries.

4.3   Introduced species such as the trees grown in conifer plantations produce a much less biodiverse ecosystem than the native broadleaved woodland.

4.4   Biodiversity has been measured in the UK over a long period by highly dedicated amateurs such as members of the Botanical Society of the British Isles. There have been national surveys of several groups of organism on at least two dates allowing a detailed picture of change in abundance over time to be built up.

4.5   To more fully understand changes in biodiversity it is necessary to develop a hypothesis that might explain the changes then collect data and carry out statistical analysis. As with any environmental information, data from biodiversity surveys show considerable variation around any mean values, making it difficult to see any overall differences.

4.6   Statistical techniques such as correlation and regression can be used to cut through this variation. These statistical tests give a significance level which is an indication of how likely the null (i.e. no difference) hypothesis is to be true. If there is a very low probability that the null hypothesis is true then there are real differences that the original hypothesis may help to explain.

4.7   Two hypotheses that deal with differing patterns of biodiversity are described in the chapter. The overlapping hotspots hypothesis asks if several different groups of organism all have their biodiversity hotspots in the same area; if true it has significant implications for designating which areas are set up as protected areas. The species–energy hypothesis predicts that the number of species is related to the amount of solar energy, with the region nearest the Equator receiving more energy and hence having more species.

4.8 It is possible to use various geographical grid systems to locate points on Earth when carrying out species surveys. The British Ordnance Survey system uses a scale of metres east or north of an origin point just south of the Scilly Isles.

Learning Outcomes for Chapter 4

When you have completed this chapter, you should be able to:

4.1 Define and use, or recognize definitions and applications of, each of the terms given in **bold** in the text. (Questions 4.3, 4.4)

4.2 Discuss Britain's international responsibilities in the area of biodiversity. (Question 4.1)

4.3 Contrast the different organizations that have measured biodiversity in the UK. (Question 4.2)

4.4 Describe and discuss scientific methods used in the study of biodiversity. (Questions 4.3, 4.4)

Questions for Chapter 4

Answer each question in about 50–100 words.

Question 4.1

Name two important habitats for which Britain has international responsibilities. Identify a key feature of each that makes it important for biodiversity.

Question 4.2

Briefly summarize how biodiversity has been measured in the UK, describing some of the organizations involved.

Question 4.3

List the main stages in testing a hypothesis. Illustrate your answer with an example.

Question 4.4

In statistics what are significance levels and why are they important?

References

Alexander, K. (1999) The invertebrates of Britain's wood pastures. *British Wildlife*, **11**, pp. 108–117.

Biological Records Centre (2002) [online] Available from: http://www.brc.ac.uk/ [Accessed 29 November 2002]

Brown, J. H. (1981) Two decades of homage to Santa Rosalia: towards a general theory of diversity. *American Zoologist*, **21**, pp. 877–888.

Burova, L. G. (1974) Ecological features of macromycetes in spruce/broadleaved forests of the Moscow region. I. Effect of the stand on the development and distribution of macromycetes. *Mikologiya i Fitopathologiya*, **8,** pp. 402–405.

Countryside Survey (2000) [online] Available from: http://www.cs2000.org.uk/ [Accessed 29 November 2002]

Fahy, O. and Gormally, M. (1998) A comparison of plant and carabid beetle communities in an Irish oak woodland with a nearby conifer plantation and clearfelled site. *Forest Ecology and Management,* **110**, pp. 263–273.

Ferris, R., Peace, A.J. and Newton, A.C. (2000) Macrofungal communities of lowland Scots pine (*Pinus sylvestris* L.) and Norway spruce (*Picea abies* (L.) Karsten.) plantations in England: relationships with site factors and stand structure. *Forest Ecology and Management*, **131**, pp. 255–267.

Flemming, L. V., Newton, A. C., Vickery J. A. and Usher, M. B. (1997). *Biodiversity in Scotland: Status, Trends and Initiatives*. Edinburgh: The Stationery Office.

Gustafsson, L., Friskesjo, A., Ingelog, T., Petterson, B. and Thor, G. (1992) Factors of importance to some lichen species of deciduous broadleaved woods in southern Sweden. *Lichenologist*, **24**, pp. 255–266.

Hale, S. E. (2001) Light regime beneath Sitka spruce plantations in northern Britain: preliminary results. *Forest Ecology and Management*, **151**, pp. 61–66.

Humphrey, J. W., Newton, A.C., Peace, A.J. and Holden, E. (2000) The importance of conifer plantations in northern Britain as a habitat for native fungi. *Biological Conservation*, **96**, pp. 241–252.

Ordnance Survey (2002) [online] Available at: http://www.ordsvy.gov.uk/ [Accessed 29 November 2002]

Project Gutenberg (2002) [online] Available at: http://promo.net/pg/ [Accessed 29 November 2002]

Stewart, A., Pearman, D. A. and Preston, C. D. (1994) *Scarce Plants in Britain*. Peterborough: JNCC.

Tree of Life Web Project (2002) [online] Available at: http://tolweb.org/tree/phylogeny.html [Accessed 29 November 2002]

UK Biodiversity Website (2001) [online] Available at: http://www.ukbap.org.uk/ [Accessed 29 November 2002]

Villeneuve, N., Grandtner, M. M. and Fortin, J. A. (1989) Frequency and diversity of ectomycorrhizal and saprophytic macrofungi in the Laurentide Mountains of Quebec. *Canadian Journal of Botany*, **67**, pp. 2616–2629.

Chapter 5 Action plans

Prepared for the course team by Mike Dodd

5.1 Introduction

In recent years one of the main responses to conserving biodiversity in Britain has been the development of **Biodiversity Action Plans (BAPs)**. This chapter outlines various types of action plan. In the UK the most important factor affecting biodiversity during the 20th century was agriculture. We discuss its impact and show how it is now linked to various schemes to protect biodiversity over the wider countryside.

As with other parts of the course this subject is constantly changing, with new or revised plans being published and policies substantially modified (this was happening almost daily at the time of writing in late 2002). To keep up to date with the subject there are several very good BAP websites (e.g. UK BAP, 2002) that should be consulted in addition to reading the text presented in the chapter.

5.2 Biodiversity Action Plans

As mentioned earlier in the course, in 1992 the United Nations Conference on Environment and Development, the 'Earth Summit', was held in Rio de Janeiro. At around this time many countries, including Britain, were trying to incorporate ideas such as sustainable development into their national policymaking systems. This conference was the focus for setting up conventions that would allow continued development but protect the Earth's natural systems. The main outcomes of the summit were:

- Agenda 21, a worldwide programme of action to achieve a more sustainable form of development throughout the 21st century.

- The climate change convention, a framework to reduce the risks of global warming by restricting greenhouse gas production.

- The biodiversity convention, a method of protecting the diversity of habitats and species around the world.

- A statement of principles on the sustainable use and management of the world's forests.

One of the most important recommendations that emerged from the conference was that each country should prepare action plans to implement the agreements. The UK Government prepared separate documents on each of the four Rio agreements and took steps towards implementation. In January 1994 the government launched a document entitled Biodiversity: The UK Action Plan. The stated overall goal of the plan was 'to conserve and enhance biological diversity within the UK and to contribute to the conservation of global biodiversity through all appropriate mechanisms'. In addition to the action plan, the government announced the setting up of a Biodiversity Steering Group with representatives from central and local government, conservation organizations, business, farming and academic bodies. The steering group was given a number of tasks including: developing costed targets for key species and habitats, improving the accessibility of biodiversity information, increasing public awareness and finally ensuring that commitments were carried out.

Reporting back on progress in 1995 the Biodiversity Steering Group identified a number of issues that, if tackled, could substantially sustain and enhance biodiversity. These included: improved management of sites, reduced applications of agrochemicals on farmland and more sensitive control of development through the planning system. However, there was one issue that needed to be addressed, without which several of the biodiversity targets could not be achieved. This was the reform of the European Community's Common Agricultural Policy (CAP) to redirect some of the expenditure towards environmental rather than purely production objectives. You will learn more about the CAP later in this chapter.

Since 1995 many 'action plans' have been prepared both at the national and local level, and preparation of these plans is an ongoing process. Action plans are directed at either conserving threatened habitats or individual species.

The 2002 Earth Summit brought together many more thousands of civil servants and world leaders but there was very little proposed action on protecting biodiversity. The only targets set were to slow the rate of species extinction by 2010, establish some marine nature reserves by 2015 and take some action to reduce pollution of the sea from land-based sources by 2004. There was also talk of restoring fisheries to their maximum sustainable yields by 2015 and generally reducing natural resource degradation. Many people felt that there should have been more specific targets covering a much higher proportion of biodiversity, in addition to those that simply prevent the rarest organisms going extinct. However, the agreements on fisheries and pollution of the sea may become increasingly important for the UK over the coming years and may ensure that our children can still have the traditional cod and chips for dinner.

5.3 Habitat action plans

Preparing the original national **habitat action plans** involved several steps. First, all habitat types in the UK were classified using definitions that could be understood by a broad range of people. Then **priority habitats** were identified using criteria that included: (a) habitats for which the UK has international obligations, (b) habitats at particular risk, for example those that have been declining rapidly, (c) habitats that provide critical services such as breeding areas for a much wider ecosystem and (d) habitats containing priority species. Given that there are always strong competing claims for any piece of land or sea within the British Isles, these priority habitats have been selected as being of high conservation concern.

Priority habitats generally have a very narrow definition within the overall scheme used for UK habitats. For example, within the broad habitat type 'rivers and streams' only chalk rivers were identified as a priority habitat. Chalk rivers are small rivers fed by water that has percolated down through the chalk bedrock. They are very rich in plant, invertebrate and fish species and are easily damaged by any form of pollution. There are many threats to these small rivers, for example from water abstraction, pollution from sewage plants or fertilizer discharge out of watercress farms.

Reedbeds are another priority habitat. There are about 5000 ha of reedbeds in the UK but the majority of this area is located in about 50 sites. They are particularly important for birds, supporting six nationally rare or 'Red Data Book' species (Figure 5.1) and providing roosting and feeding areas for migratory species. There are also five Red Data Book invertebrates associated with reedbeds. Box 5.1 introduces Red Data Books.

Figure 5.1 A bearded tit (*Panurus biarmicus*), a Red Data Book species that lives in reedbeds.

Box 5.1 Red Data Books

The International Union for the Conservation of Nature and Natural Resources (IUCN) produces Red Data Books or 'red lists' of species threatened with global extinction. Each country also produces its own, more detailed, red lists that should use the same criteria as the IUCN lists. These criteria have been developed through a series of iterations by IUCN's Species Survival Commission. Categories and criteria used are phrased so as to present an easily understood system for classifying species at high risk of global extinction. The guidelines are intended to be consistent, objective and allow comparisons between widely different taxa. The categories are widely recognized internationally (Chapter 1, Section 1.3.3). The 'threatened' categories (Figure 5.2) — critically endangered, endangered and vulnerable — are defined using a set of quantitative criteria. Taxa meeting any one of the criteria qualifies it for that level of threat.

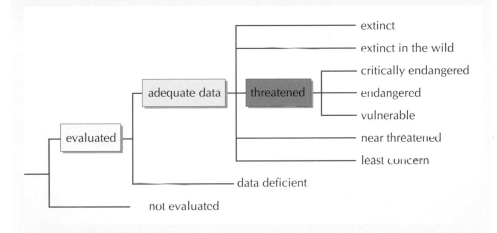

Figure 5.2 The IUCN categories for classifying species at risk.

Originally species were selected to go in the Red Data Book based only on their distribution records from sources such as the 1962 *Atlas of the British Flora* (Perring and Walters, 1962). For example, in 1967 a detailed survey was undertaken of the species occurring in 15 or fewer 10 km squares from the *Atlas*. The results were published in 1977 as *British Red Data Book 1: Vascular Plants*. Now the IUCN criteria include quantitative measurements of population size and geographic area and quantitative analysis of the probability of extinction. These measures give a more accurate estimate of the likelihood of a species going extinct and thereby allow improved policy and conservation decisions.

Full details of the threat categories, problems of scale and methods of dealing with data uncertainty can be downloaded from the IUCN red lists website (IUCN, 2002). Further details on the red lists programme in general and a searchable database of threatened plants and birds can be found at the Red Lists organization website (IUCN Red List, 2002).

5.3.1 Local habitat action plans

Looking at reedbeds further, one way to find out if the national plan is performing at individual sites is to examine the local action plans, as these will have details of what is actually happening on the ground at individual sites. The example used here is from the April 2002 Oxfordshire local biodiversity action plan. Archaeological evidence suggests that reedbeds were once extensive among the floodplains of the river Thames along its journey through the county, but now there are no large areas of this habitat left at all. The Oxfordshire BAP gives a target of an additional 40 ha of reedbeds as their contribution to the national target of an additional 1200 ha. There has already been some progress with a number of new schemes to extend and create new reedbeds. Two large sites were listed in the April 2002 version of the action plan: Otmoor with 22 ha of new reedbed proposed and Rushy Common with 15.5 ha proposed. The Otmoor scheme is a partnership between the Royal Society for the Protection of Birds (RSPB) and the Environment Agency and part of a much larger government-sponsored project to turn 200 ha of farmland into a mosaic of wetland habitats.

The local action plan (Oxfordshire Nature Conservation Forum, 2002) provides more detailed costings, target dates and information about key organizations involved, which include English Nature, Oxfordshire County Council, the local Wildlife Trust (Berkshire, Buckinghamshire and Oxford Wildlife trust), RSPB, Oxford Nature Conservation Forum and other NGOs.

5.4 Single-species BAPs

In addition to habitat action plans, the UK BAP instigated **individual species action plans**. It is often these species action plans that hit the headlines, raising public awareness and bringing in sponsorship. The otter, dormouse, red squirrel, bittern, skylark, natterjack toad, lady's slipper orchid and large blue butterfly are some of the 'popular' species that have national action plans. Within this list there are contrasting reasons for setting up action plans — the orchid and bittern are extremely rare while the large blue was extinct in Britain and is being reintroduced. By contrast skylarks are still common in parts of Britain but have been in sharp decline due to loss of their habitat and food sources as a result of agricultural intensification. This decline is apparent across the skylark's range in Europe and may lead to the species becoming rare if it cannot be halted.

Just as with habitats, individual species also have local action plans. One species with a BAP in the county of Buckinghamshire is the green-winged orchid (*Orchis morio*; Figure 5.3). It was chosen because it is a 'charismatic' species and is a good indicator of species-rich meadows, a habitat that has severely declined in recent years. Figure 5.4 is a distribution map for *O. morio* in Britain as a whole (Stewart et al., 1994). Figures 5.5 and 5.6 show the distribution of *O. morio* in Buckinghamshire since 1987.

The initial question that the British distribution map (Figure 5.4) prompts is 'why use this species as an indicator as it seems so common?' Indeed in the past it was described as one of the commonest plants in Europe. However, if the data are examined more closely it soon becomes apparent that these maps can be misleading. The 100 km grid squares do not contain large numbers of populations as they would with a very common species such as the daisy (*Bellis perennis*). Instead there are now just a few isolated species-rich meadows where the plants still occur. Frequently even the 2 km squares represent just one small site. Zooming in still further and looking at a 100 m × 100 m section of one field, individual orchids are seen to have large spaces between them (Figure 5.7).

Figure 5.3 The green-winged orchid (*Orchis morio*).

For a population to be maintained over the long term there needs to be gene exchange between individuals — pollen has to be transferred from one plant to the stigma on another by a suitable insect and fertilization follows so that seed can be set. Orchids also need a suitable fungal partner for the seed to develop into a flowering plant. Without both the suitable insect and fungal partner present the orchid will become extinct. In 1926 when Druce compiled his flora of Buckinghamshire, he stated that *O. morio* was common and widespread (Druce, 1926): there has probably been an 80–90% decline in its abundance since then.

The decline in *O. morio* in Buckinghamshire has been largely due to loss of suitable habitat. Many other species such as the pasque flower (*Pulsatilla vulgaris*) have suffered a similar fate and now survive only as small isolated populations. When a species is reduced to this point other factors come into play in addition to gross habitat loss. The size of these populations of plants and indeed other organisms such as insects, varies from year to year. This is known as **population variability**. In some years there are many orchid flowering spikes but in other years there are few. This variation is particularly important if the mean population size is small, as the number of individuals could easily fall to zero. If not replenished by immigration from other areas the species would become locally extinct. If populations are isolated from each other then each will eventually decline to zero and, over time, the national population will slowly vanish. By measuring the background year-to-year variation in population size it is possible to get an idea of how long isolated populations will persist. For example,

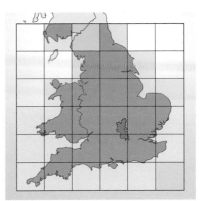

Figure 5.4 Distribution of *O. morio* in Britain. The species is present in all the 100 km × 100 km grid squares in England and Wales (shown in purple) except one (marked green); it is not present north of the area shown.

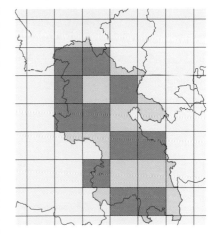

Figure 5.5 Distribution of *O. morio* in Buckinghamshire (indicated by a darker region in Figure 5.4) using a 10 km × 10 km grid.

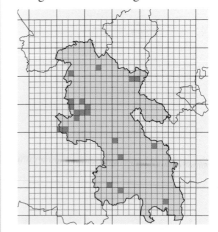

Figure 5.6 Distribution of *O. morio* in Buckinghamshire using a 2 km × 2 km grid.

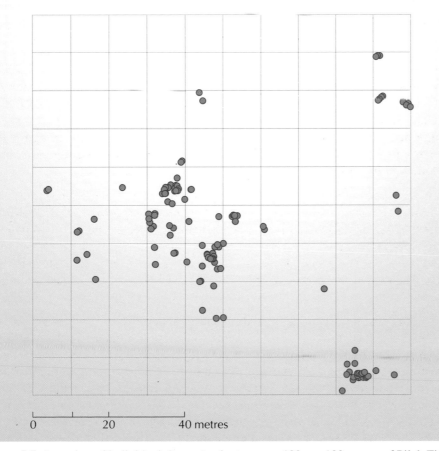

0   20   40 metres

Figure 5.7 Location of individual *O. morio* plants over a 100 m × 100 m area of Pilch Field nature reserve in Buckinghamshire.

if there is a lot of variation the population is likely to hit zero and go extinct quickly. Alternatively a population with the same mean size but a smaller amount of year-to-year variability may persist for many years.

The background variation in population size of *O. morio* was measured as counts of flowering spikes each year over 27 years from a meadow in Lincolnshire (Gillman and Dodd, 2000). Year-to-year variability in population size, measured over these 27 years, can be used directly to predict time to extinction. This background variability can also be combined with knowledge of various aspects of the species biology to produce a mathematical model of the number of flowering spikes each year (Figure 5.8).

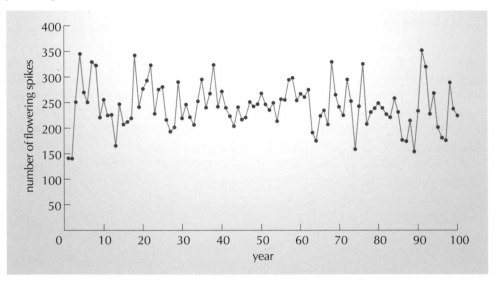

Figure 5.8 Model of population variability of *O. morio* over a 100-year period.

In Figure 5.8 the population size fluctuates between limits of about 150 and 350 flowering spikes but over the 100 years that the computer model was run it did not go extinct. Just looking at this particular run of the computer model you could imagine that if you went into the field and recorded the plants each year between years 4 and 13, the steep decline would make you extremely concerned that the population was going extinct. But this run of bad years is simply part of the natural variation. Once there is a suitable model various scenarios can be tested by varying different parts of the model and seeing what effect there is on the predicted population size and its long-term persistence. For example, it would be possible to see what effect different land management strategies might have on the orchids.

Models such as these have indicated that to protect some mobile species it may be necessary to link together small populations, for example by establishing corridors of suitable habitat, so that if the population at one site goes extinct it can be recolonized from another one. The idea of linking small population patches is particularly important for conserving biodiversity of insects such as butterflies.

Ideally, accurate models of population variability would be available for all species with BAPs but to produce them requires many years of data collection and a detailed understanding of the biology of each species. The *O. morio* population model includes some aspects of the species ecology but there are still many other factors to take into account since the orchid has a complex life history. It takes several years to mature from seed to flowering plant; individuals can re-flower for a few years, or can stop flowering and remain dormant underground for a couple of years before re-flowering and dying. These life-history details were observed by following a large number of individual plants over several years and the research obviously took a considerable amount of effort.

Many aspects of biodiversity monitoring and the development of biodiversity action plans are extremely labour intensive and may require years of dedication and expertise. NGOs and individual volunteers, because they can provide enthusiasm, dedication and expertise, have a key role in biodiversity action. They are also ideally placed to provide publicity and carry out the type of direct campaigning that local authorities are not able to do.

⬤ Imagine you are a concerned citizen and want to 'do something about biodiversity' in your local area. Describe some of the actions you might take.

⬤ Your first task might be to find out more about the topic of biodiversity. You are already doing that by studying this course and searching the Internet for information. There are several organizations, such as a local wildlife trust or natural history society that you could join. These organizations will probably run a programme of talks and visits to nature reserves and be able to assist if you wanted to record species. They may also be involved in writing the local biodiversity action plan. To get involved in habitat management there are organizations such as the British Trust for Conservation Volunteers who go out each week with groups of volunteers and physically carry out management tasks to help with species conservation. There are several national campaigning organizations such as Greenpeace and Friends of the Earth who may have local representatives. Besides local issues such as trying to save a local nature reserve these national organizations are often good at pointing out links between, for example, the new hardwood doors in the local council offices and illegal, unsustainable logging and loss of biodiversity in tropical rainforests.

5.5 Business and biodiversity

In addition to the action plans being developed by national and local government, businesses and other organizations are producing strategies to minimize their impact on biodiversity. Businesses can have many detrimental effects on biodiversity — using products from endangered or over-harvested species, polluting the environment or building on species-rich habitats. It is, however, possible for a company to be managed so that it has a much smaller impact on the environment, for example by encouraging the maintenance of biodiversity on its land or by influencing its suppliers and consumers to consider biodiversity. Some of Britain's largest companies are taking these issues seriously and have produced detailed action plans, whereas others are doing only the bare minimum to comply with legislation and any sustainability requirements that their consumers put on products supplied.

Apart from any benefit to wildlife, action plans are often used in public relations exercises to promote the company's green image and potentially boost sales. However, in some cases action plans have also identified methods of working and building that actually save the company considerable sums of money, for example by investment in low-energy input buildings and developing a more pleasant working environment.

There are some very helpful websites if you want to investigate this topic further, e.g. the Business and Biodiversity Resource Centre (2002).

You should now go to the Web and do the activities associated with this chapter.

5.6 The changing face of agriculture — action to protect biodiversity in the wider countryside

So far in this chapter there has been considerable discussion of action plans and how they might help to protect species and habitats in certain areas. However, there has been little mention of the wider countryside of Britain and the major changes in agricultural practice during the course of the 20th century that have had profound effects on the environment.

During the 20th century until World War II farming was generally in deep depression, mainly as a result of cheap imports of agricultural products. During this period there were few tractors and no combine harvesters and about 1.6 million ha of land was used just to support working horses. This picture changed during the war when the government launched schemes to encourage food production in Britain to feed the besieged population. Mass-produced tractors started replacing horses and there was a new period of land drainage, allowing previously waterlogged areas to be cultivated. The effect on wildlife was generally negative as it was the land that had become neglected and reverted to 'rough grassland' during the depressed years that supported a greater diversity of species that was ploughed up to feed the nation during time of war. However, the major changes to farming, and to wildlife (Figure 5.9), started during the 1960s and continued for much of the rest of the century, with the accelerating

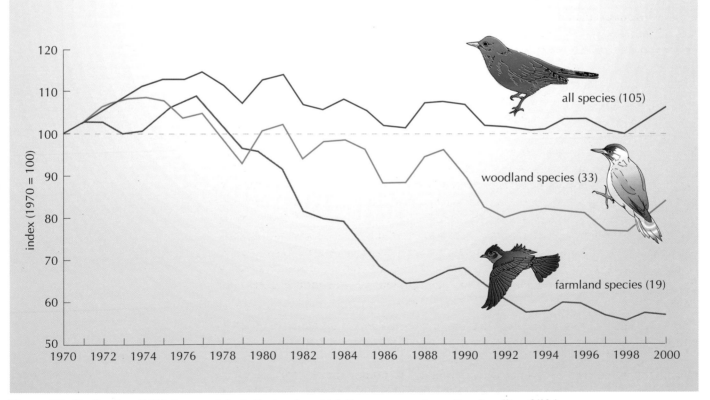

Figure 5.9 Decline in wild birds, one of the indicators by which the government monitors 'quality of life'.

process of agricultural intensification. Fields were amalgamated to accommodate the new combine harvesters (Figure 5.10) and larger tractors with the loss of hedgerows and ditches. More fertilizers and pesticides were used. Farms became larger and so did machinery, which meant that fewer people were needed. Many of these changes were driven by production-orientated incentives particularly associated with the Common Agricultural Policy.

Figure 5.10 The introduction of machines such as combine harvesters, which operate efficiently only on large fields, led to the widespread removal of hedgerows.

An indication of how much farming had changed can be seen in a study by Taylor et al. (1993) who, in the early 1990s, looked at the energy budget of a typical mixed arable and dairy farm. At the beginning of the 20th century the farm would have seen virtually no inputs from pesticides, no modern fossil-fuel-driven machinery and little, if any, mineral fertilizer. Yet on the farm by the end of 20th century the energy required to produce all the fertilizers and pesticides and drive the machinery totalled 13.3 Terajoules (TJ) per year (a Terajoule, 10^{12} J, is a large unit of energy equivalent to the energy content of approximately 24 tons of crude oil), while the total output of farm produce was the equivalent of 21.2 TJ. This meant that there was a net harvest of about 7.9 TJ of energy from the Sun (21.2 TJ − 13.3 TJ) by plants on the farm. During the course of the 20th century yields of wheat have increased three- to fourfold through plant breeding to produce varieties that do well if they are given very high doses of fertilizers and protection from diseases by pesticides. If this change in yield is taken into account then the net energy harvested from the Sun each year by crops on the farm has changed very little over the years; today's higher yields are simply the product of a much greater use of fossil fuels. Fossil fuels are of course a finite resource and produce greenhouse gases when they are burned. Plants take up carbon dioxide as they grow so you might expect the modern farm to be a net consumer of CO_2; however, the energy required for fertilizers, machinery and intensive animal production means that the farm actually produced 3.8 times the amount of greenhouse gases that it absorbed.

From the energy analysis it is clear that modern agriculture is all about high-input, high-output production. Successive policies by the government and the European Community (EC) via the CAP have fostered higher production through a series of measures, including very generous guaranteed minimum prices for the main commodities. The original aim was to even out year-to-year uncertainty in production and price and ensure that Europe was self-sufficient in the staple food items.

However, during the 1980s it became increasingly clear that the policies were too successful, and what appeared to be vast stockpiles of cereals, beef and wine were building up. The public was complaining about subsidies given to farmers, especially as it appeared that it was the already rich corn barons who were being given most of the handouts. Payment followed production, so that those who produced the most, that is owned the most land and therefore were likely to be the most wealthy, received the largest payments. There was also frustration that British taxpayers' money seemed to be going to the unelected EC bureaucracy in Brussels, only to be given back to farmers to enable them to rip out hedgerows, create even bigger fields and reap even more subsidies with the resulting higher yields, all at the expense of the environment.

Eventually things changed. The level of subsidies through direct price support for commodities was brought down and altered to area or headage payments (for livestock) and at the same time set-aside schemes were introduced. Set-aside land could not be used for producing the main crops and it was normally left fallow for one year or used for non-food crops. However, it has been argued that headage payments are among the most damaging subsidies, as they make overgrazing almost obligatory. With the reduction in subsidies, farm incomes, from farming alone, are at a 30-year low and some farmers now derive more income from alternative ventures such as farm-based bed and breakfasts or other rural enterprises. The combination of increasing awareness of environmental issues in the British countryside and the low farm incomes has led to the government and EC developing a series of agri-environment schemes that can be applied to large tracts of land and are not simply directed at individual species. Two of the larger schemes are the Environmentally Sensitive Areas scheme and Countryside Stewardship which were funded in 2001–2 to the tune of £51 million and £48 million, respectively. Farmers participating in these projects receive an income in return for enhancing the environment. There are also moves to further redistribute money from the CAP into a much wider range of rural economic activities than farming alone, and to increase greatly the scope and funding of agri-environment schemes. In 2002 the government's report on Farming and Food stated

> …we do not think there will be any places in a small country like England where there is no measurable public good from protecting and enhancing the countryside, and where the environment can be consequently written off.

> (Report of the Policy Commission on the Future of Farming and Food, 2002)

There has also been considerable debate about what type of agriculture, if any, should be subsidized with the £3 billion a year spent on agricultural support in the UK. The countryside of Britain, as a whole, relies on farming for its distinctive character and several habitat types such as hay meadows and chalk downland also rely on correct farming management to maintain their species diversity. Now that purely production-orientated incentives are no longer in vogue, the question is how to decide on what type of farming is required and who should make the decisions. In 2001 after a foot-and mouth epidemic extending throughout the UK, the government set out to develop a wide public consultation on the whole future of farming, food and their long-term sustainability. There is a very wide range of possible views from the food industry and farming communities themselves, from those interested in access to the countryside, those interested in biodiversity, and the hunting lobby. There is also the view that there should be no subsidies of any kind in the countryside, and that market forces should direct everything.

- What effect might removal of all subsidies of any kind have on biodiversity in the wider countryside?

- Biodiversity may increase in the abandoned areas but decline still further in the more intensively cultivated parts of the country.

In New Zealand where subsidies were suddenly removed from farming, there was a change to more intensification in some areas, but other areas that were less suitable for growing crops or grazing were turned into vast single species forests of introduced pine trees. Both of these changes had a negative effect on biodiversity. However, it is possible that pockets of land less suited to agricultural production could be simply abandoned and become wildlife habitat until the next turn of the economic cycle. Subsidies have often been used in an attempt at overcoming the uncertainty of economic cycles and to even out both the level of food production and farming incomes.

A public consultation exercise may suggest a working countryside where all the benefits of each type of agriculture are recognized. For example, along a river there may be water meadows producing hay early in the year, which is then grazed by stock, but with the value of the meadows as flood protection for the local town recognized. On drier land there may be a mixed rotation of crops with limited pesticide and fertilizer inputs including a zero pesticide strip round the edge of fields. In hilly areas there may be livestock production although not at excessively high stocking density. Mixed in with these farms there could be woodland and various other rural enterprises (Figure 5.11). In all cases the farming type would be further adapted to

Figure 5.11 Diverse countryside showing farming, woodland and other habitats.

local conditions. This picture may be generally recognized as a good method of managing the wider countryside, but how do you design a policy that would actually work to achieve it? Designing a policy and set of subsidies to increase production is relatively easy but achieving something more sustainable right across the country is much more of a challenge. It is a challenge that policymakers really do need to take up as farmers, land managers and much of the general public can have great difficulty with concepts such as biodiversity and need more guidance on how their day-to-day actions affect local diversity. However, it is also important to recognize that land managers can require very detailed local knowledge of soils, climate and other factors, knowledge that is often held by existing landholders rather than external specialists. Setting arbitrary targets in terms of overall biodiversity is very unlikely to tap into this local knowledge.

At the beginning of the 21st century it is a very interesting time for the countryside of Britain. There are substantial changes in the direction of agriculture, turning from purely production orientated schemes to much more sustainable systems. The government is looking for ways in which all sectors including the general public can be involved in policy decisions. It is also a time when there is a greater understanding than ever before of biodiversity and its loss. What better time could there be to form links between sustainable food production systems and a healthy biodiverse environment?

5.7 Summary of Chapter 5

5.1   Biodiversity Action Plans were originally developed in response to the 1992 Earth Summit in Rio. They have become one of the main ways of protecting the environment in the UK.

5.2   Habitat action plans have been prepared for all priority habitats (habitats of high conservation concern), e.g. reedbeds. Plans may lead to the protection of existing areas of these habitats and the establishment of new areas of these habitats.

5.3   Individual species have action plans for a variety of reasons but mainly either because they are very rare or because they are in sharp decline. To develop good action plans for individual species, detailed monitoring and modelling of population variability would ideally be available. However, this takes many years of detailed measurements. An example of a species with a BAP is the natterjack toad.

5.4   Local action plans have been developed by a wide range of different organizations to protect the local habitats and species. These plans are partly designed to help meet national targets for species and habitat conservation.

5.5   Many businesses can have large negative effects on the environment. A variety of large and small companies have developed plans to minimize their impact. Some have found that developing a BAP increases overall efficiency by reducing waste and creating a better environment to work in.

5.6   Agricultural intensification was the biggest threat to biodiversity in the UK during the 20th century. This intensification was often fuelled by government subsidies. There is now greater emphasis on sustainability which may benefit biodiversity or at least reduce its rate of loss.

Learning Outcomes for Chapter 5

When you have completed this chapter you should be able to:

5.1 Define and use, or recognize definition and applications of, each of the terms given in **bold** in the text. (Questions 5.1–5.5)

5.2 Discuss, illustrated by examples, how BAPS are produced, how they operate and what effect they may have on biodiversity and ecosystems. (Questions 5.1–5.5)

Questions for Chapter 5

Answer the following questions in no more than 100 words each.

Question 5.1

Contrast, illustrated by examples, the UK national biodiversity action plan with the biodiversity action plan for a local authority.

Question 5.2

Discuss, by reference to named examples, how biodiversity action plans can aid sustainability of ecosystems.

Question 5.3

Discuss, by reference to named examples, the role of partnerships and participation, particularly from non-government organizations, in biodiversity action plans.

Question 5.4

Discuss uncertainty in relation to biodiversity action plans for single species, giving examples.

Question 5.5

Discuss examples of the positive and negative effect of UK agriculture on biodiversity during the 20th century.

References

Business and Biodiversity Resource Centre (2002) [online] Available from: http://www.businessandbiodiversity.org/ [Accessed 18 December 2002]

Druce C. G. (1926) *Flora of Buckinghamshire*. Arbroath: T. Bunce and Co.

Gillman, M. P. and Dodd, M. E. (2000) Detection of delayed density dependence in an orchid population. *Journal of Ecology*, **88**, pp. 204–212.

IUCN (2002) [online] Available from: http://www.iucn.org/themes/ssc/redlists/rlindex.htm [Accessed 18 December 2002]

IUCN Red List (2002) [online] Available from: http://www.redlist.org/ [Accessed 18 December 2002]

Oxfordshire Nature Conservation Forum (2002) [online] Available from: http://www.oncf.org.uk/ [Accessed 18 December 2002]

Perring, F. H. and Walters, S. M. (eds) *1962 Atlas of the British Flora*. London: Thomas Nelson & Sons.

Perring, F. H. and Farrell, C. (1977) *British Red Data Books: Vascular Plants*. Lincoln: Society for the Promotion of Nature Conservation.

Report of the Policy Commission on the Future of Farming and Food (2002) [online] Available from: http://www.cabinet-office.gov.uk/farming/index/CommissionReport.htm [Accessed 18 December 2002]

Stewart, A., Pearman, D. A. and Preston, C. D. (1994) *Scarce Plants in Britain*. Peterborough: JNCC.

Taylor, A. E. B., O'Callaghan, P. W. O. and Probert, S. D. (1993) Energy audit of an English farm. *Applied Energy*, **44**, pp. 315–335.

UK BAP (2002) [online] Available from: www.ukbap.org.uk [Accessed 18 December 2002]

Answers to Questions

Chapter 1

Question 1.1

Biodiversity is 'all hereditarily based variation at all levels of organization'. It includes the genetic variation found within species and the community of species that forms the living component of an ecosystem. An ecosystem is a community of species plus its physical environment, all connected by transfers of carbon and other chemical elements. The carbon cycle is the pathway by which this element moves within and between ecosystems. Exchange of CO_2 with the atmosphere links all ecosystems into the global carbon cycle.

Question 1.2

An aesthetic appreciation of nature can create economic value in conserving biodiversity when, as in the case of eco-tourism, people are prepared to pay to visit or conserve natural habitats. A desire for a varied diet or for the natural products of, for example, rainforests, can also create a market that could help to conserve biodiversity, provided the exploitation is sustainable.

Question 1.3

Perhaps the chief uncertainty lies in poor information about how many species there are in the first place. Probably the next most important source of uncertainty arises from the lack of information about the size and extent of populations of known species. Finally, even when the precise numbers of individuals in a population are known, it is not possible to translate this into a definite prediction of whether that species will survive or not because numbers fluctuate over time, particularly when small. Predictions about population sustainability, and hence about extinction rates, are therefore always probabilistic and uncertain.

Question 1.4

Genetically variable crop populations tend to be less susceptible to disease, and therefore the long-term sustainability of crop yields can depend on the preservation of biodiversity at the genetic level of organization.

Chapter 2

Question 2.1

Your list of keywords should include most of the following: development, knowledge, global, degradation, ecosystem, resource, biodiversity, sustainable, scientific, policies, institutions, management, trade-offs, evaluation.

Question 2.2

The words used on p. viii of *WR* are:

> Adopting this 'ecosystem approach' means we evaluate our decisions on land and resource use in terms of how they affect the capacity of ecosystems to

sustain life, not only human well-being but also the health and productive potential of plants, animals, and natural ecosystems. Maintaining this capacity becomes…our passage to a sustainable future.

This passage is central to the whole purpose behind *WR*, which is to evaluate the state of ecosystems in order to demonstrate that current trends in exploitation are unsustainable. The purpose is explicitly political, but the claims are based on scientific evidence that can be objectively evaluated.

Question 2.3

Your list should include most of the following: agriculture, forestry, fishing, fibre production, water purification, watershed protection, climate control, soil production, carbon sequestration, nutrient cycling, medicines, pollination, genetic diversity.

Question 2.4

Your list should include most of the following: overfishing, forest fragmentation, coral reef destruction, pollution, overpumping of groundwater, conversion of natural habitats to agriculture, invasive organisms, urban expansion, overexploitation of game animals, deforestation, climate change.

Question 2.5

This point is discussed on *WR* p. 16. Ecosystems often have *thresholds* that, once crossed, may cause a sudden collapse without warning. There is inherent *uncertainty* in such systems (see Book 1, Chapter 3). Lack of sufficient knowledge about ecosystem function also makes predicting the threshold between sustainable exploitation and collapse all the more difficult to forecast.

Question 2.6

Subsidies can cause a resource such as irrigation water to be over-exploited and wasted (e.g. in the western USA) or lead to the overuse of pesticides (e.g. in Indonesia) (see p. 30).

Question 2.7

Regulations, Sectoral Divisions and Corruption are the three other types of 'policy failure' discussed (see pp. 31, 33). For example, land-use regulations may permit development without regard to environmental costs; ecosystem management may be divided between different departments of government and thus make an integrated approach difficult; corruption allows illegal timber extraction from supposedly protected forests to occur on a massive scale in Indonesia.

Question 2.8

Five tools are mentioned on p. 32. They are (i) actual market prices (e.g. for fish), (ii) the cost of replacing an ecosystem service (e.g. water purification), (iii) price differences between property with/without amenities (e.g. proximity of a house to the sea), (iv) the amount of money and time spent by visitors in a natural area, and (v) 'contingent valuation', based on what people say they would be prepared to pay to prevent a natural area being developed. Two limitations of this approach are that markets may not exist for the goods/services provided by an ecosystem, and some may be 'priceless'.

Question 2.9

A trade-off can be thought of as the costs that must be paid to acquire a benefit of some kind. In the case of eco-tourism, discussed in *WR* pp. 34–35, the environmental benefits of this activity are that it may create income, which will provide local people with an incentive to conserve their natural ecosystems. The trade-off is that the economic activity generated by eco-tourism can itself be damaging in various ways.

Question 2.10

These issues are complicated (*WR* pp. 33–41), but the most fundamental point is whether or not the owners of resources perceive it to be in their interests to exploit them sustainably.

(a) It appears that the closer owners are to the land and the longer their association with it, the more likely they are to exploit it sustainably. Thus, traditional owners, such as indigenous communities in Indonesia, may exploit their forest sustainably, but new owners of forest land, whether in northern California or in developing countries, often just clear-fell it (p. 33).

(b) Adaptation to environmental and social changes involves people in taking measures that improve the ability of ecosystems to support them. The incentive and ability to do this are greater when the resources are owned or controlled by those who depend on them (pp. 38–39).

Chapter 3

Question 3.1

(a) Apparently freshwater: of the four parameters assessed, conditions were rated bad, poor, fair and good.

(b) Forest: this is the only ecosystem in which one service (production of food/fibre) shows an increasing capacity whereas all other measured capacities are decreasing or unknown, probably as a consequence of exploitation.

Question 3.2

The current condition for relevant goods and services ranges from good to fair or poor (and in one case bad) but, out of the 24 cases where it was assessed, changing capacity is increasing in only one, mixed in two and decreasing in all the rest.

Question 3.3

Biodiversity is clearly in the worst state (condition poor or bad in three of the five ecosystems and only fair in the other two; capacity decreasing in all). Water quality is the next worst (condition poor or fair in the four ecosystems where it was assessed and capacity decreasing in three of the four).

Question 3.4

The information is mainly in Box 2.1 (p. 45) and on p. 46 (The 'Big Picture', but with limitations).

- The three main indicators of ecosystem health used in the study do not cover all aspects of health.

- The indicators do not provide information about the capacity of ecosystems to remain healthy.

- Capacity indicators are difficult to obtain or unobtainable.

- The PAGE study was at a global level and not the national or more local scale needed by resource managers. Although it aimed to produce an integrated ecosystem assessment, the PAGE study does not because it focuses on types of ecosystem (forests, etc.) rather than on geographical regions (e.g. the Amazon) containing many ecosystems.

Question 3.5

Conversion, general pollution (including eutrophication) and habitat destruction or damage. The information is mainly in *WR* pp. 82–83 and in the case studies (Chapter 3).

Question 3.6

Habitat fragmentation, global climate change, new pathogens and overharvesting are all mentioned in *WR* as contributing factors, with air pollution as a further possibility. Higher temperatures due to global climate change were mentioned as probably the main cause of increased coral mortality. There is no evidence that acid rain is a significant factor but, although ozone depletion is not mentioned in *WR*, you may recall from Book 1 that there are concerns about the effects of UV-B radiation on (especially) Antarctic phytoplankton, seabirds and mammals.

Question 3.7

(i) South Florida, USA: the seagrass meadows have been largely destroyed because of altered salinity (caused by reduced water flow from the inland region); general pollution (especially higher concentrations of nutrients) has probably also contributed to this decline. Note that other changes in the South Florida ecosystem relate mainly to terrestrial or freshwater biodiversity.

(ii) St Lucia, the Mankòtè mangrove: illegal dumping, spraying with insecticides against mosquitoes and tree-cutting for charcoal (which could also be regarded as a form of over-harvesting) have all contributed to degradation of the mangrove forest.

(iii) The Philippines, Bolinao coral reefs: destructive fishing practices (use of dynamite and cyanide) were identified as the main factor.

Question 3.8

The approach in southern Florida is essentially *top down*, i.e. it is driven and funded by the state and federal governments. The cost runs into billions of dollars and involves the army. By contrast, at Mankòtè the approach was *bottom up*: it was a regional NGO (non-governmental organization) that formulated a plan and organized local people to execute it, with tacit government support and no outside funds. A similar bottom-up approach was used at Bolinao: researchers at a local university informed and galvanized local people both to oppose damaging development (the cement factory) and develop a long-term management plan.

Question 3.9

Conversion to other uses, especially in Africa, South America and Asia and especially for tropical forest.

From the map on *WR* p. 91, note that forest area is actually increasing in the developed world, most markedly in Europe. This is largely due to the planting of conifers. In the UK, the planting of new, broad-leaved woods for both timber and amenity is also increasing.

Question 3.10

Disturbance and destruction, e.g. by logging or fire (*WR* p. 96); habitat fragmentation (see, for example, the maps on *WR* pp. 94–95); and invasive species, which on *WR* p. 99 are ranked as second only to habitat conversion in importance.

You may have thought that air pollution and, more specifically, acid rain should be included but, although significant in Europe and parts of North America, they have had little impact in the tropics where the largest areas of forests occur.

Question 3.11

Habitat destruction mainly due to overuse, especially overgrazing by cattle and over-harvesting by both legal and illegal logging.

Question 3.12

General pollution, especially with nutrients such as phosphate and nitrates; damage (e.g. through water abstraction, dams, channelling of rivers); invasive species (*WR* p. 118 and also the South African case study, p. 193).

Question 3.13

Conversion has severely affected wetlands, many of which have been drained for agricultural use (see *WR* p. 106–107). Habitat fragmentation, e.g. by dam construction that blocks fish movements, is a consequence of draining and other damage (*WR* p. 108): the Mekong case study (p. 208) illustrates the severity of the threat. Over-harvesting is mentioned as a threat in the Mekong River basin (*WR* p. 113) although, globally, aquaculture (which poses its own threats, such as nutrient pollution) is taking over from the harvesting of wild fish.

Threats due to new pathogens or parasites are illustrated by, for example, the disastrous effects of crayfish plague, a pathogen that affects native British crayfish and derives from the introduced signal crayfish. Air pollution and the linked threat posed by acid rain are not mentioned in *WR*, but you may know from previous studies or general knowledge that inputs of nitrogen from air pollution contribute to eutrophication and the air pollution which leads to acid rain has caused widespread damage in the past to rivers and lakes in Europe and North America.

Question 3.14

Dams provide cheap hydroelectric power and the countries which benefit most are China, Laos and, to a lesser extent, Thailand. 'Downstream' countries (Cambodia and Vietnam) might benefit if they could more easily buy cheap electricity via a regional grid system. Diversion for irrigation purposes benefits (or would benefit) mainly China and Thailand.

Question 3.15

(a) Fish production and biodiversity would be reduced, affecting particularly Cambodia and Vietnam but all countries to some degree. Agricultural production in the lowland floodplains could be reduced owing to both reduced silt deposition (because of lower flows) and incursion of salt water; again Cambodia and Vietnam are most affected. Dams displace people from their homes causing great social disruption particularly in the 'upstream' countries China, Laos and Thailand.

(b) For this large-scale, transnational system, a top-down approach involving regional or national governments is required. The Mekong River Commission (MRC) represents such an approach, the snags being that China and Myanmar (Burma) are only observers and the MRC has no power to enforce recommendations. The MRC has also been largely unsuccessful at coordinating regional interests and developing plans for sustainable water use.

Question 3.16

(i) The need to maintain the quality of drinking water for New York City. (ii) Money!: watershed protection and building new filter plants are the only options for (i) and the former is much cheaper.

Question 3.17

(i) Conversion to intensive agriculture and urban use has been very extensive; (ii) habitat fragmentation (compare, for example, the two maps on *WR* p. 126 to see the impact of roads on grasslands in America) is arguably the second most important factor but could be ranked equally with conversion; (iii) grassland biodiversity has also been reduced or damaged in several other ways, including tourism, illegal hunting (e.g. in parts of Africa), excessive, human-induced fires and overgrazing. Alien species are mentioned in *WR* as being another threat, and air pollution is yet another.

Question 3.18

(a) In coastal (*WR* p. 69) and polar ecosystems (*WR* p. 136).

(b) In coastal ecosystems, higher sea temperatures are thought to be a cause of coral bleaching and rising sea levels will destroy some ecosystems (e.g. mangroves) and could damage others (e.g. coral reefs). In polar ecosystems, possible effects on biodiversity mentioned in *WR* include altered availability of food and changed fish diversity. In the Arctic there are already indications, for example, that the earlier melting of ice does not allow polar bears sufficient access to seals, their main source of food at the beginning of the year.

Question 3.19

Some examples you might have thought of are:

Ecosystem that has an effect	Ecosystem that is affected	Description/example
Forest	Freshwater	Forest ecosystems affect the quality (nutrient and sediment inputs) and quantity of water entering freshwater ecosystems; e.g. New York City watersheds, South African watersheds.
Agricultural	Freshwater	Agricultural ecosystems affect water quality, mainly via nutrient (and sometimes sediment) inputs from run-off; e.g. Florida Everglades.
Freshwater	Coastal	Affects salinity and nutrient levels; e.g. Florida Everglades.
Urban	All types	Air pollution leading to nitrogen inputs, acid rain and ozone depletion; sewage and storm-water particularly affect freshwater ecosystems.
Grassland	Freshwater	Affects the quality and quantity of water entering rivers and underground water reserves; this effect is not assessed in *WR* but widely believed to be significant.
Mountain	Freshwater	Forest cover and soil stability affect the quality and quantity of water reaching lowlands (*WR* p. 134).

Chapter 4

Question 4.1

Two important habitats for which Britain has international responsibilities are estuaries and ancient trees. Estuaries provide important ice-free over-wintering areas for migratory wading birds. Ancient trees provide a habitat for several endangered insects, lichens and fungi.

Question 4.2

Dedicated amateur naturalists have collected most of the records of plants and animals in the UK. The government has also funded random sampling programmes to obtain a representative idea of biodiversity from all areas. However, this sampling is much less complete than, for example, that carried out by the Botanical Society of the British Isles or the British Trust for Ornithology.

Question 4.3

The main stages in testing a hypothesis are data collection, data analysis, and drawing conclusions. You may then go on to further refine the hypothesis and re-test it. Two examples are testing the overlapping hotspots hypothesis and the species–energy hypothesis.

Question 4.4

Statistical analysis produces two main types of output. The first type, numbers such as correlation coefficients or regression coefficients, describe the relationship between variables. The second type, significance levels, give an indication of how likely the relationship is to be true. Significance levels are important because they help us decide if a relationship is likely to be correct or just the result of random chance. It is incorrect to simply give a correlation coefficient to support a hypothesis without giving any indication of significance as it is not possible to determine how robust the conclusion is.

Chapter 5

Question 5.1

The UK national BAP sets out a framework covering all habitats and species found in the United Kingdom. Within these, priority habitats and species are identified and costed habitat action plans and species action plans produced. Local action plans identify locally important species and habitats but also work towards national priorities. Local action plans detail individual sites and activities and local people can get involved in producing them and making sure they are carried out. An example of a national BAP would be the habitat BAP for chalk rivers and streams or the individual species BAP for the lady's slipper orchid. An example of a local action plan would be the plan for the green-winged orchid in Buckinghamshire.

Question 5.2

All BAPs should clearly state how the ecosystem will be sustained, otherwise there would be little point in the action plan. For example, in the reedbed action plan, reedbeds themselves will be sustained by cutting, scrub removal and protection from pollution. Reedbeds may be able to help the wider ecosystem by reducing agricultural pollution and providing a renewable resource — reed for thatching. All of this is in addition to their role in supporting rare bird and insect species and providing migrants with feeding and roosting sites.

Question 5.3

One of the main features of BAPs is the involvement of partner organizations. The UK national plans include national organizations such as the Countryside Commission for Wales, Scottish Natural Heritage, National Rivers Authority, English Nature, each of which will need to carry out some action for the plan to succeed fully. Local plans are usually sponsored by a wide range of NGOs with very varied involvement including providing sponsorship, carrying out practical conservation work, collecting species records or actually writing the plan itself.

Question 5.4

More is probably known about the habitats and species of the UK than anywhere else in the world. However, there is still uncertainty in the action plans. Costed habitat action plans often have a broad range of potential costs to the taxpayer and there is considerable uncertainty about future agricultural policy and how this might affect the net costs. For example, the 2001 outbreak of foot-and-mouth disease led to the re-evaluation of long-term habitat management with livestock over large parts of Britain. Single-species action plans, especially for plants, are often based on a limited number of surveys with little information on year-to-year fluctuations in population size. Better understanding of species management for long-term survival can be obtained by detailed year-on-year monitoring and developing population models that incorporate key aspects of the species biology.

Question 5.5

Most of the land area of the UK is maintained in some way by the agricultural system. The meadows that supported large numbers of species, including green-winged orchids in the earlier part of the 20th century, were created for grazing animals. However, as the agricultural system became more intensive with higher inputs of fertilizers, much of the diversity in these meadows was lost, leaving just a few high-yielding grasses. Increasingly intensive agricultural systems have greatly reduced biodiversity over many parts of the UK. However, there are now moves towards more sustainable agricultural systems that both produce food and benefit wildlife while at the same time ensuring a reasonable income.

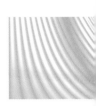

Acknowledgements

Grateful acknowledgement is made to the following sources for permission to reproduce material in this book:

Chapter 1

Figure 1.1: Masefield, G. B. et al. (1969) *Fruits, The Oxford Book of Food Plants*, Oxford University Press; *Figure 1.3*: © Martin Sanders; *Figure 1.5*: Groombridge, B. and Jenkins, M. D. 'Biodiversity at country level (UNEP)', Global Biodiversity, Earth's Living Resource in the 21st Century, © 2000 World Conservation Monitoring Centre; *Figure 1.6*: © Wilhelm Barthlott (Professor Dr., Botanic Institute and Botanic Gardens, University of Bonn, reproduced by permission); *Figure 1.7*: Groombridge, B. and Jenkins, M. D., 'Diversity of freshwater fishes', Global Biodiversity, Earth's Living Resources in the 21st Century. © 2000 World Conservation Monitoring Centre; *Figures 1.9–1.12*: Houghton, J. T. et al. (2001) *Climate Change 2001 The Scientific Basis*, Cambridge University Press. Copyright © 2001, Intergovernmental Panel on Climate Change; *Figure 1.15*: Carpenter, S. R. and Kitchell, J. F. (1993) *The Trophic Cascade in Lakes*, Cambridge University.

Chapter 4

Figures 4.1, 4.3, 4.8–4.10: Courtesy of Mike Dodd; *Figure 4.7*: HIP/British Library (Heritage Image Partnership).

Chapter 5

Figures 5.1, 5.3, 5.10, 5.11: Courtesy of Mike Dodd.

Every effort has been made to trace all the copyright owners, but if any has been inadvertently overlooked, the publishers will be pleased to make the necessary arrangements at the first opportunity.

Index

Entries in **bold** are key terms. Page numbers referring to information that is given only in a figure or caption are printed in *italics*.